Welcome to BASIC Grammar

1

KUMSUNG

About This Book

개념 학습

➕ 초등학생이 꼭 알아야 할 문법 개념을 쉽게 설명해요.

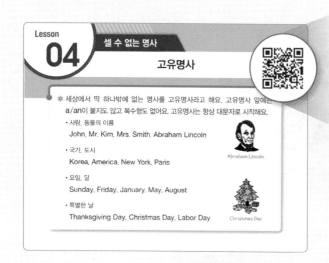

모바일 강의 예시

친구들의 문법 도우미! 니콜 선생님의 쉽고
재미있는 설명을 들으면 문법 개념이 머리에
쏙쏙! 문법 실력은 쑥쑥!

PC www.englishbuddy.kr에서도
볼 수 있어요.

문제 풀이

➕ Quick Check-Up ➡ 다양한 유형의 exercise ➡ Fun Wrap-Up 순으로 문제를 제시하여 체계적
으로 학습할 수 있어요.

Step 1

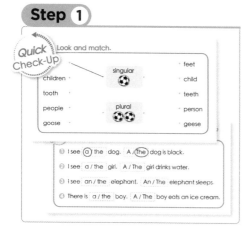

간단한 문제를 풀어보며 문법 개념을 잘
이해했는지 확인해요.

Step 2

다양한 유형의 문제를
풀어보며 실력을 다져요.

Step 3

미로 찾기, 색칠하기 등
재미있는 활동으로 학습한
내용을 복습하며 마무리해요.

Contents 1

Chapter

명사

1

Welcome to Basic Grammar

I can do it!

문장의 특징

✿ 주어와 동사를 포함하고 있고, 하나의 완전한 의미를 가진 것을 '문장'이라고 해요. 문장에는 주어와 동사가 필요해요.

<u>I</u> <u>walk</u> to school. (문장 ○)   In the house (문장 ✕)
주어 동사

✿ 문장의 첫 글자는 대문자로 시작하고, 문장의 끝은 문장의 종류에 따라 마침표 . 나 물음표 ? 또는 느낌표 ! 등을 찍어 줘요.

The baby sleeps . 　　　　 **I** see the sky .
대문자 　　　　　　　　　　　대문자

> 주어는 주체를 나타내는 '누가, 무엇이', 동사는 동작이나 상태를 나타내는 '~하다, ~이다'에 해당하는 부분이에요.

Quick Check-Up

Check the *sentences*.

☑ I like my bike. 　　　　 ☐ I like my bike

☐ play in the park. 　　　 ☐ We play in the park.

☐ to school 　　　　　　 ☐ I go to school.

☐ The baby can speak. 　☐ the baby can speak.

☐ Mom is in the store. 　☐ Mom is in the store

문장의 특징

A Look and match.

1. I have   soccer.

2. They play   two brothers.

3. The snow is   play together.

4. Five girls   white.

5. Today is   my birthday.

B Correct and rewrite.

1. ~~we~~ are friends.   We are friends.

2. **it** is a dog. _____

3. You are kind _____

4. **the** boys play games. _____

5. I love my mom, _____

6. The sun is bright _____

 Find and follow the *sentences*.

I love my friend.

You help me.

In the car

I have a book.

a red mouse

I see my friend.

I have

the snow

문장의 종류

- ✿ 설명하는 문장의 끝에는 항상 마침표 **.** 를 찍어요.

The elephant is big **.**   I am a student **.**

- ✿ 질문하는 문장의 끝에는 항상 물음표 **?** 를 써요.

Is it a pen **?**   Is he your father **?**

Where is my pen **?**   Can you swim **?**

Quick
Check-Up

Circle the correct ones.

① the / The dog is small.

② Can / can you swim?

③ Are / are you a student?

④ is / Is he your father?

⑤ where / Where is my pen . / ?

⑥ I / i am 10 years old.

⑦ mom / Mom sits on the grass . / ?

문장의 종류

A Read and mark ○ or ✕.

1. I can run ⬚

2. My dog is small. ⬚

3. i am tall. ⬚

4. What is your name. ✕

5. Where are you? ⬚

B Correct and rewrite.

1. ~~he~~ can run fast. He can run fast.

2. **are** you cold? _____

3. **they** are thirsty. _____

4. **can** you dance? _____

5. **is** it a chair? _____

6. **i** am hungry. _____

Look and color.

| . | 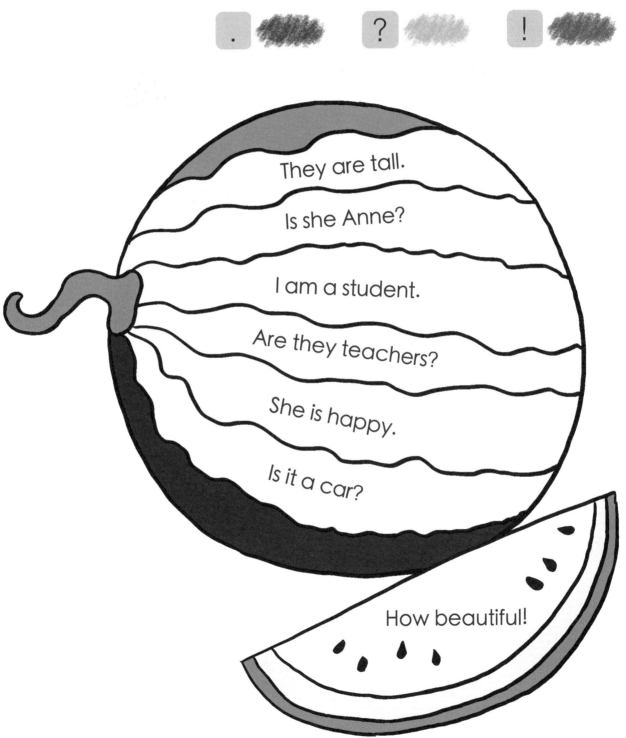 | ? | | ! | |

They are tall.

Is she Anne?

I am a student.

Are they teachers?

She is happy.

Is it a car?

How beautiful!

명사란?

✿ 명사란 사람, 동물, 사물, 장소 등의 이름을 가리키는 말이에요.

people 사람	girl	man	teacher	things 사물	pen	hat	car
animals 동물	dog	bird	mouse	places 장소	house	school	market

Quick Check-Up

Check the *nouns*.

• noun 명사

☐ house	☑ dog	☐ park	☐ bag
☐ pen	☐ go	☐ bird	☐ is
☐ teacher	☐ in	☐ of	☐ market
☐ see	☐ school	☐ come	☐ eat
☐ car	☐ hat	☐ mouse	☐ girl

명사란?

A Look and write.

pen　　　pencil　　　mom　　　school
girl　　chair　　market　　friend　　house

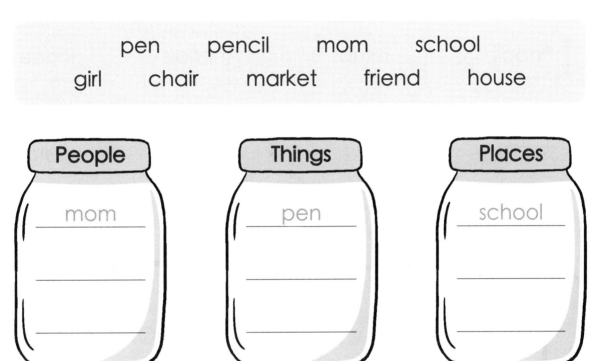

People	Things	Places
mom	pen	school
___	___	___
___	___	___

B Look and check.

① People	✓ⓐ boy	ⓑ desk	ⓒ apple
② Animals	ⓐ hand	ⓑ chair	ⓒ rabbit
③ Things	ⓐ eraser	ⓑ cat	ⓒ playground
④ Places	ⓐ sister	ⓑ ruler	ⓒ school

명사란?

People	Things	Animals	Places
FATHER	CRAYON	LION	SCHOOL
STUDENT	HAT	DOG	HOUSE

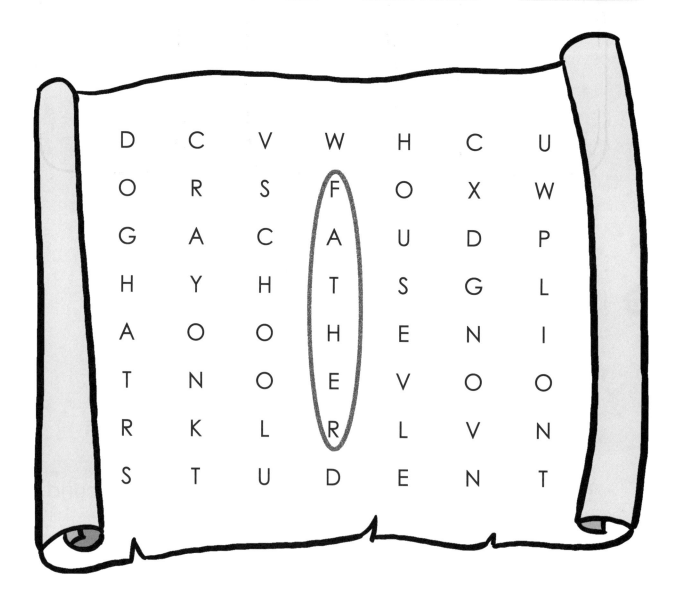

D C V W H C U

O R S F O X W

G A C A U D P

H Y H T S G L

A O O H E N I

T N O E V O O

R K L R L V N

S T U D E N T

a/an + 단수 명사

✿ 명사는 '고양이, 사과'처럼 셀 수 있는 명사와, '희망, 사랑'처럼 셀 수 없는 명사가 있어요. 셀 수 있는 명사가 하나일 때는 a 또는 an을 붙여요.

- a + 자음으로 시작하는 단수 명사

  a brother, **a** classroom, **a** cat, **a** pen, **a** banana

 a cat

- an + 모음(a, e, i, o, u)으로 시작하는 단수 명사

  an eraser, **an** ant, **an** apple, **an** egg

 an apple

'단수'는 하나,
'복수'는 둘 이상을 뜻해요.

Quick Check-Up — Circle the correct ones.

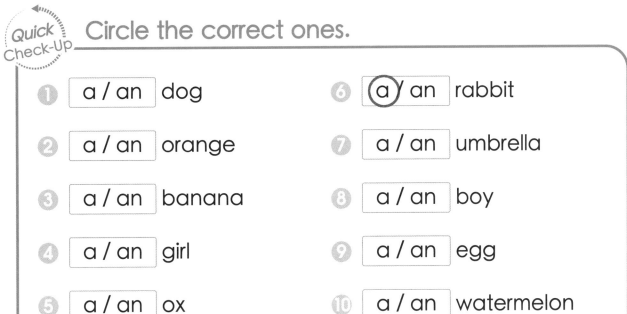

❶ a / an dog

❷ a / an orange

❸ a / an banana

❹ a / an girl

❺ a / an ox

❻ (a) / an rabbit

❼ a / an umbrella

❽ a / an boy

❾ a / an egg

❿ a / an watermelon

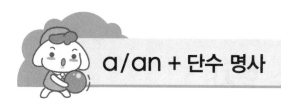

a/an + 단수 명사

A Read and mark ○ or ×.

① I have a apple. ·· ☒

② I buy an eraser. ··· ☐

③ She eats a orange. ·· ☐

④ I need a umbrella. ·· ☐

⑤ I want a cat. ·· ☐

B Read and match.

① I am _____ student.

② I have _____ egg.

③ I need _____ toy car.

④ Tom sees _____ ant.

⑤ They want _____ watermelon.

a

an

Color the apple tree.

a ▓▓▓▓   an ▓▓▓▓

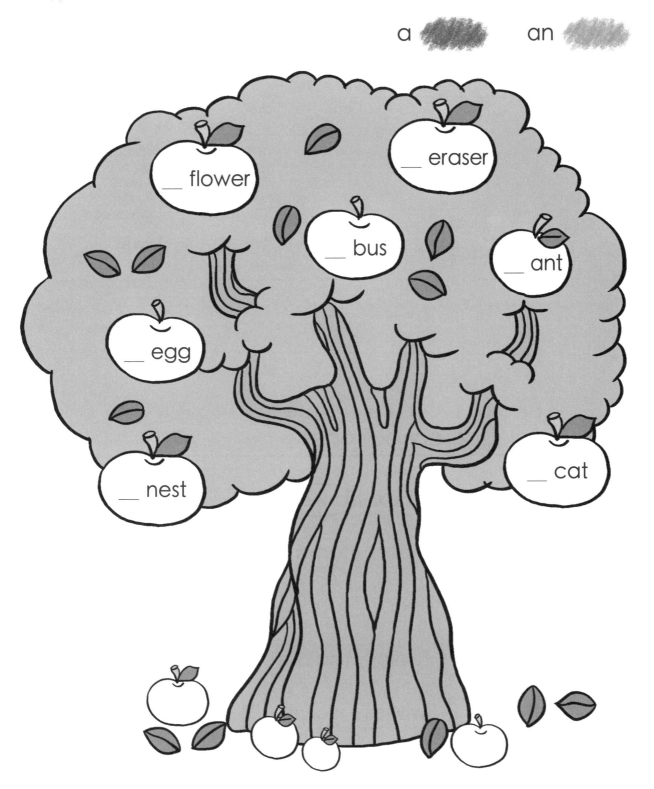

__ flower

__ eraser

__ bus

__ ant

__ egg

__ nest

__ cat

명사의 복수형: 규칙

✿ 셀 수 있는 명사가 두 개 이상일 때는 -s나 -es를 붙여서 복수형을 만들어요. 단어 형태에 따라 만드는 방법이 아래와 같이 달라져요.

대부분의 명사	-s	bag	→	bag**s**
-s, -ch, -sh, -x로 끝나는 명사	-es	dish	→	dish**es**
[자음+o]로 끝나는 명사	-es	potato	→	potato**es**
[자음+y]로 끝나는 명사	-y → -ies	baby	→	bab**ies**
[모음+o]로 끝나는 명사	-s	kangaroo	→	kangaroo**s**
-f(e)로 끝나는 명사	-f(e) → -ves	leaf life	→ →	lea**ves** li**ves**

Quick Check-Up

Circle the correct ones.

① box   boxs / (boxes)

② tomato   tomatos / tomatoes

③ school   schools / schooles

④ radio   radios / radioes

⑤ wolf   wolfes / wolves

A Read and write.

-s	-es	-ies	-ves
① pear	① bus	① berry _berries_	① half
② note	② dish	② baby	② wolf
③ girl	③ watch	③ lady	③ shelf

B Look and mark ○ or ✕.

① I wash the dishs. .... ✕

② My mom tells us many stories. .... ☐

③ Knifes are dangerous. .... ☐

④ Here come two buses. .... ☐

⑤ She has two babys. .... ☐

 Color the blocks with correct words.

churches	rosees	wifes	heroes
hats	cates	bikeiess	dishes
vases	girles	balles	boys
calves	spoons	rulers	apples

① How many blocks did you color? _____

② What letter did you make? _____

Lesson 03

셀 수 있는 명사

명사의 복수형: 불규칙

✿ 셀 수 있는 명사라 하더라도 -s나 -es가 붙지 않는 불규칙한 경우가 있어요.

• 단수 명사와 복수 명사의 형태가 다른 경우

foot	→ feet	tooth	→ teeth
goose	→ geese	ox	→ oxen
child	→ children	mouse	→ mice

a mouse → mice

• 단수 명사와 복수 명사의 형태가 같은 경우

fish → fish   deer → deer   sheep → sheep

fish의 또 다른 복수형 fishes는 물고기의 종류가 여럿일 때 사용해요.

• 복수형으로 쓰는 명사(짝을 이루는 명사)

scissor**s**   glass**es**   pant**s**   short**s**   pajama**s**

 Look and match.

foot		feet
children	**singular**	child
tooth		teeth
people	**plural**	person
goose		geese

A Read and write.

| children | teeth | geese | feet | mice |

1 I have 24 _____ .

2 There are five _____ in the room.

3 My _____ are painful after walking.

4 I see many _____ in the lake.

5 The cat chases three _____ .

B Correct and rewrite.

1 I wear **a glass**.   glasses

2 I have some **pant**. _____

3 We have many **box**. _____

4 **Childs** love toys. _____

5 I need **a scissor**. _____

Complete the puzzle.

shorts   fish   sheep   children   women

셀 수 없는 명사

고유명사

🌸 세상에서 딱 하나밖에 없는 명사를 고유명사라고 해요. 고유명사 앞에는 a/an이 붙지도 않고 복수형도 없어요. 고유명사는 항상 대문자로 시작해요.

• 사람, 동물의 이름

John, Mr. Kim, Mrs. Smith, Abraham Lincoln

Abraham Lincoln

• 국가, 도시

Korea, America, New York, Paris

• 요일, 달

Sunday, Friday, January, May, August

• 특별한 날

Thanksgiving Day, Christmas Day, Labor Day

Christmas Day

Quick Check-Up — Check the correct ones.

☐ Mr. Lee	☐ mrs. smith	☑ Mike	☐ Koreas
☐ paris	☐ Sunday	☐ america	☐ Christmas
☐ a Monday	☐ May	☐ Seoul	☐ Friday
☐ labor day	☐ July	☐ busan	☐ August

고유명사

A Correct and rewrite.

① My name is ~~amily~~.

Amily

② It is **a Tuesday**.

③ Yesterday was **may** 2.

④ Today is **children's day**.

⑤ They are from **japan**.

B Read and write.

| Saturday | David | Christmas | Seoul | February |

① My mom's birthday is in ___ February ___.

② My uncle lives in ___ S ___.

③ The party is on ___ S ___.

④ His name is ___ D ___.

⑤ We sing carols at ___ C ___.

 고유명사

 Answer the questions and introduce yourself.

Introduce Yourself

1. What is your name?

   _____

2. What is the name of your best friend?

   _____

3. What is the name of your teacher?

   _____

4. When is your birthday?

   _____

5. What is your favorite holiday?

   _____

It's all about you.

04 셀 수 없는 명사

물질명사, 추상명사

❋ 셀 수 없는 명사에는 고유명사뿐만 아니라 물질명사와 추상명사가 있어요.

- 물질명사: 특정한 모양이 없어서 셀 수 없는 명사
  - 액체: water, milk, coffee, oil, juice, tea
  - 가루: rice, sugar, salt, sand, flour
  - 기체: air, gas, smoke
  - 고체: gold, silver, paper, beef
  - 날씨: rain, snow, wind

water

- 추상명사: '사랑, 아름다움, 시간' 등 형태가 없고 추상적인 의미를 나타내는 명사
  love, hope, friendship, beauty, music,
  art, time, power...

music

Quick Check-Up — Check the *uncountable* nouns.

• uncountable 셀 수 없는

☐ millk	☑ love	☐ salt	☐ hope
☐ people	☐ a chair	☐ snow	☐ oil
☐ English	☐ bread	☐ time	☐ a car
☐ coffee	☐ pants	☐ water	☐ cats
☐ a pen	☐ art	☐ schools	☐ a boy

 물질명사, 추상명사

Ⓐ Look and mark ○ or ✕.

1. I listen to music. ⬜
2. I buy two sugars. ✕
3. We have water. ⬜
4. They have good friendships. ⬜
5. I put a rice in the pot. ⬜
6. I have two coffees. ⬜

Ⓑ Look and match.

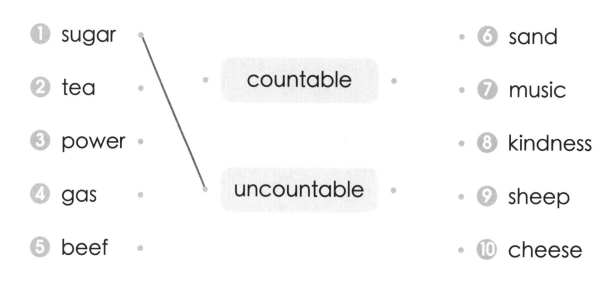

1. sugar
2. tea
3. power
4. gas
5. beef

countable

uncountable

6. sand
7. music
8. kindness
9. sheep
10. cheese

Cut and put.

Countable Nouns

a zoo

Uncountable Nouns

friendship

※ 아래와 동일한 카드가 173쪽에 있습니다. 해당 페이지의 카드를 사용하세요.

friendship	water	a zoo	wind	a dog	rulers	a ball	a mouse
mice	a bike	bikes	teeth				

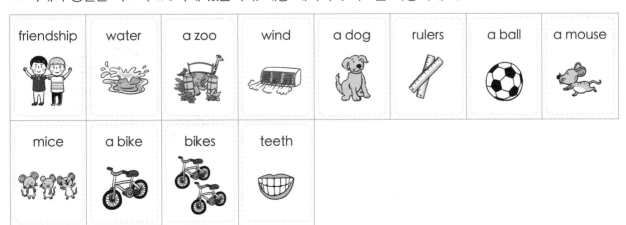

Go to p. 173

물질명사 수량 표현

단수

✿ 셀 수 없는 물질명사는 '담는 그릇'이나 '모양'을 기준으로 셀 수 있으며,
[a+단위+of+물질명사]로 나타내요.

• 그릇으로 세기

a cup of coffee
a glass of water
a can of coke
a bowl of rice
a bottle of juice
a bag of flour

• 모양으로 세기

a piece of pizza / cheese
a slice of pizza / cheese
a sheet of paper
a loaf of bread
a bar of soap

Quick Check-Up — Circle the correct ones.

❶ a (glass) / bag of water

❷ a can / piece of coke

❸ a bowl / loaf of bread

❹ a cup / bag of coffee

❺ a sheet / bowl of paper

❻ a bowl / loaf of rice

단수

A Read and write.

| water | cake | rice | juice | pizza |
| soup | milk | cheese | cereal |

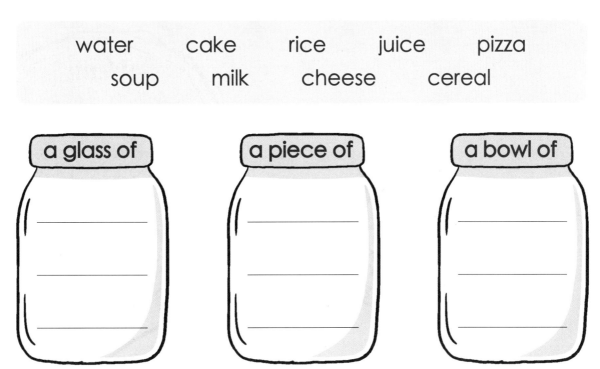

a glass of

_____
_____
_____

a piece of

_____
_____
_____

a bowl of

_____
_____
_____

B Look and match.

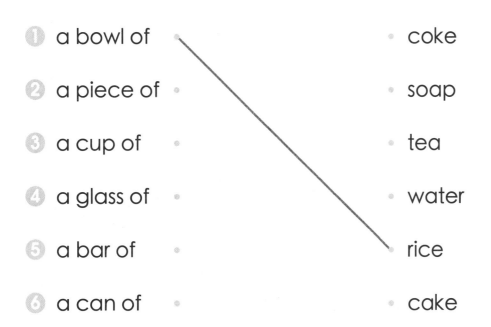

1. a bowl of   • coke
2. a piece of   • soap
3. a cup of   • tea
4. a glass of   • water
5. a bar of   • rice
6. a can of   • cake

 Look and draw.

Menu
- a bowl of rice
- a piece of cheese
- a bottle of juice
- a loaf of bread
- a glass of water

물질명사 수량 표현

복수

❋ 셀 수 없는 물질명사는 '담는 그릇'이나 '모양'을 기준으로 수량을 나타내요. 담는 용기 등이 둘 이상일 때는 [수량＋단위＋s/es＋물질명사]로 나타내요.

a cup of coffee	→ two cup**s** of coffee
a bottle of wine	→ two bottle**s** of wine
a can of soda	→ two can**s** of soda
a loaf of bread	→ two loa**ves** of bread
a tube of toothpaste	→ two tube**s** of toothpaste
a bowl of rice	→ two bowl**s** of rice
a piece of pizza	→ two piece**s** of pizza
a slice of pizza	→ two slice**s** of pizza

Quick
Check-Up

Look and match.

❶  •

❷ •

❸ •

• three cups of

• two tubes of

• two bowls of

복수

A Look and mark ○ or ✗.

1. I drink two bottles of wine. ○

2. I buy three bowls of toothpaste.

3. She eats four pieces of cake.

4. I need four cups of coffee.

5. They have five glasses of soup.

B Read and write.

bowls of	glasses of	pieces of
loaves of	cups of	cans of

1. Mom buys two _____ bread.

2. Dad drinks two _____ tea.

3. I eat three _____ cheese.

4. He has two _____ rice.

5. We need four _____ milk.

6. I buy two _____ coke.

Follow and write.

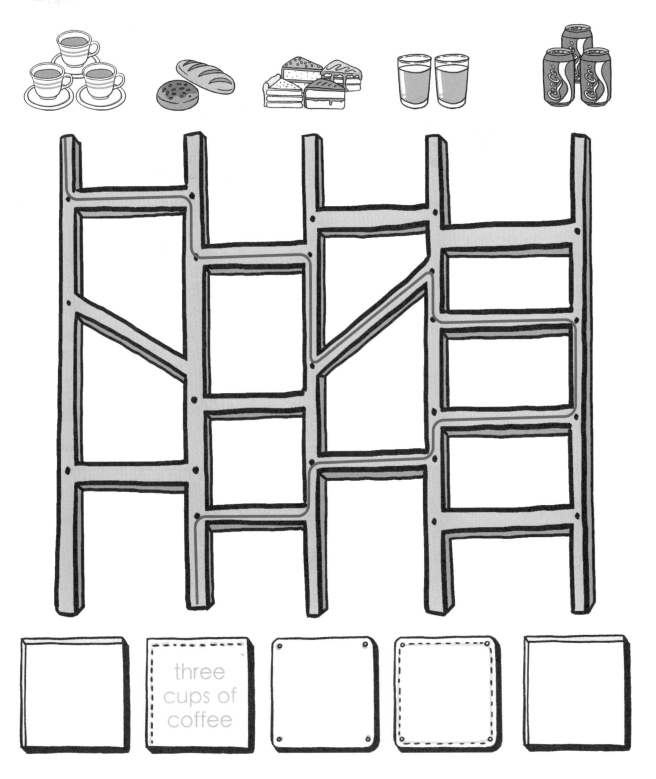

three
cups of
coffee

부정관사 a, an

❋ a, an은 여러 개 중에서 '정해지지 않은 하나'를 가리킬 때 써요.
명사의 첫소리가 자음일 때는 a를 쓰고, 명사의 첫소리가 모음(a, e, i, o, u)
일 때는 an을 써요.

a book
자음

an elephant
모음

a   an

Quick Check-Up — **Check the correct ones.**

☐ a book   ☐ a ant

☐ an elephant   ☑ a chair

☐ a cat   ☐ an car

☐ an igloo   ☐ an pen

☐ a pear   ☐ an orange

부정관사 a, an

A Read and circle.

①  （a） / an ball

②  a / an apple

③  a / an bag

④  a / an ant

⑤  a / an tree

⑥  a / an umbrella

B Read and match.

① arm

② table

③ octopus

④ sock

⑤ ant

a

an

⑥ picture

⑦ orange

⑧ ruler

⑨ elephant

⑩ car

 부정관사 a, an

 Choose and write the word with *a* or *an*.

an   apple

_____ _____

_____ _____

_____ _____

_____ _____

_____ _____

_____ _____

_____ _____

| mouse | bird | hat | elephant |
| ant | apple | car | umbrella |

38 Chapter 1

a, an, the

✦ 셀 수 있는 명사 중에서 '정해지지 않은 하나'를 가리킬 때에는 부정관사 a/an을 쓰고, 이미 앞에서 언급한 것이나 특정한 것을 가리킬 때에는 정관사 the를 써요.

• **a**: 셀 수 있는 명사가 하나이고, 첫소리가 자음일 때

a bag (○) a bags (×) an bag (×)

• **an**: 셀 수 있는 명사가 하나이고, 첫소리가 모음(a, e, i , o, u)일 때

an eraser (○) an erasers (×) a eraser (×)

• **the**: 셀 수 있는 명사, 셀 수 없는 명사 앞에 모두 쓸 수 있어요.

– 셀 수 있는 명사 앞에: the cat (○) the cats (○)

– 셀 수 없는 명사 앞에: the hope (○) the milk (○)

 Quick Check-Up Circle the correct ones.

① I want a / an book.

② My mom wants a / an dog.

③ I see a / an elephant.

④ She likes an / the short stories.

a, an, the

A **Read and write.**

a	the / The	an

① I see ____a____ monkey in the zoo.

② I read a book.

_____ book is interesting.

③ I need an umbrella.

_____ umbrella looks good.

④ I eat _____ apple every day.

⑤ I live in _____ big city.

B **Read and mark ○ or ✕.**

① I see a octopus in aquarium. ⟶ ✕

② Kitty is an lazy cat. ⟶ ☐

③ I eat a pieces of cake. ⟶ ☐

④ I write an letter to my friend. ⟶ ☐

⑤ There is an cat on the street. ⟶ ☐

Fun Wrap-Up! Choose and color.

a 　　an 　　the / The

I like （a / the） rainy day.

I tell you a / an story.

An / The cat is big.

I like a / an orange.

I need an / the book.

They go on a / an picnic.

정관사 the (1)

* '정해진'이라는 의미를 가진 정관사 **the**는 '바로 그'라는 뜻으로 앞에 나온 명사를 다시 언급할 때 사용해요.

I see **a** puppy.　　**The** puppy is white.

* 정관사는 말하는 사람과 듣는 사람이 서로 알고 있는 것을 나타낼 때도 써요.

Open **the** window.　　　　Close **the** door.

* 정관사 **the**는 뒤에 오는 명사의 첫소리가 모음(a, e, i, o, u)으로 시작할 때에는 [ði]라고 발음해요.

the egg　　**the** elephant　　**the** answer　　**the** orange

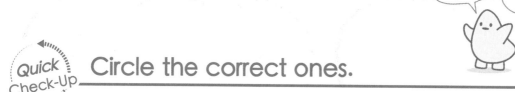

Quick Check-Up ── Circle the correct ones.

① I see [(a) / the] dog. [A / (The)] dog is black.

② I see [a / the] girl. [A / The] girl drinks water.

③ I see [an / the] elephant. [An / The] elephant sleeps.

④ There is [a / the] boy. [A / The] boy eats an ice cream.

정관사 the (1)

A Correct and rewrite.

1 I see a cat. ~~A~~ cat is cute.　The cat is cute.

2 Look at **a** bird in the sky.　＿＿＿＿＿＿＿＿＿＿＿＿

3 Lock **a** door, please.　＿＿＿＿＿＿＿＿＿＿＿＿

4 I see a dog. **A** dog is big.　＿＿＿＿＿＿＿＿＿＿＿＿

5 Open **a** window.　＿＿＿＿＿＿＿＿＿＿＿＿

B Read and match.

1 I have ＿＿＿＿ puppy.

2 I know ＿＿＿＿ answers.　　　　　　a

3 There is a duck in the river.
＿＿＿＿ duck is white.　　　　an

4 I want ＿＿＿＿ puppy.　　　　　　the

5 Look at ＿＿＿＿ moon.

 정관사 the (1)

 Read and write.

John wants ___a___ comic book.

He goes to _____ Fun Comic bookstore.

He looks at many comic books there.

He sees one comic book.

He picks _____ comic book.

He likes _____ comic book.

He buys _____ comic book.

정관사 the (2)

❋ 정관사 the를 꼭 써야 하는 경우
- 유일한 것 앞에: **the** sun, **the** moon, **the** earth
- 방향과 위치 앞에: to **the** east, to **the** west, to **the** right, to **the** left
- 악기 앞에: I play **the** violin / piano / guitar.

❋ 정관사 the를 쓰지 않는 경우
- 고유명사 앞에: ~~the~~ John, ~~the~~ New York
- 식사 앞에: have ~~the~~ breakfast, have ~~the~~ lunch
- 운동 종목 앞에: play ~~the~~ baseball, play ~~the~~ tennis
- 과목 앞에: study ~~the~~ English, study ~~the~~ math

play ~~the~~ tennis

Quick Check-Up · Check the correct ones.

☐ the sun   ☐ to the east

☐ play the piano   ☑ the moon

☐ have the dinner   ☐ study math

☐ Mike   ☐ to the right

☐ play the tennis   ☐ have the lunch

정관사 the (2)

A Read and mark ○ or ✕.

1. The balloon is in the air. ⎯⎯⎯⎯⎯⎯⎯⎯ ○

2. My sister lives in the Japan. ⎯⎯⎯⎯⎯⎯ ☐

3. I have the breakfast. ⎯⎯⎯⎯⎯⎯⎯⎯ ☐

4. You go to the right. ⎯⎯⎯⎯⎯⎯⎯⎯ ☐

5. Suzy plays the piano. ⎯⎯⎯⎯⎯⎯⎯ ☐

6. I play the tennis. ⎯⎯⎯⎯⎯⎯⎯⎯ ☐

B Read and choose.

1. There is | moon / the moon | in the sky.

2. I throw a ball in | air / the air |.

3. We eat out for | dinner / the dinner |.

4. My brother plays | basketball / the basketball |.

5. I study | English / the English | very hard.

Circle the words that need the word *the*.

Help me find a banana, please.

English   guitar   west   sun

sky

tennis

left

east   art   moon   lunch   math

John   world

A Choose the correct answers.

1 I want _____ book.

① two ② an ③ a

2 She eats _____ orange.

① a ② an ③ two

3 I know _____ answers.

① a ② the ③ an

4 She has two _____.

① babys ② babies ③ babyes

5 _____ love toys.

① Children ② Childs ③ Childes

B Fill in the blanks.

a	an	the	The

1 I see _____ monkey in the zoo.

2 I read a book. _____ book is interesting.

3 I eat _____ apple every day.

4 She plays _____ piano.

C Unscramble the sentences.

1   a watermelon. / want / They

_____

2   parents. / are / These / my

_____

3   mom's birthday / My / is / in February.

_____

4   We / four / milk. / glasses of / need

_____

D Answer the questions.

1   What do you eat every day?

_____

2   How many teeth do you have?

_____

3   When is your birthday?

_____

4   What day is it today?

_____

Chapter

대명사

2

I can do it!

인칭대명사

단수: I, you, he/she/it

🔅 명사를 대신하는 말을 '대명사'라고 하고, 사람이나 사물을 대신하는 말을 '인칭대명사'라고 해요. 가리키는 대상이 누구인지에 따라 인칭대명사가 달라져요.

I	you	he, she, it

말하는 사람: 나	듣는 사람: 너	그 외 다른 대상: 그/그녀/그것

Quick Check-Up Circle the correct ones.

단수: I, you, he/she/it

A Read and match.

1. you
2. I
3. it
4. he
5. she

B Look and write.

I   he   she   you   it

1. _____
2. _____
3. it
4. _____
5. _____

단수: I, you, he/she/it

Look, write, and make.

※ 아래와 동일한 전개도가 173쪽에 있습니다. 해당 페이지의 전개도를 사용하세요.

they

they
I
you
he
she
it

Go to p. 173

인칭대명사

복수: we, you, they

🌸 가리키는 대상이 하나가 아니고 여럿일 때에는 인칭대명사의 복수형을 써요.

we	**you**	**they**

나를 포함한 '우리'	상대방을 포함한 '너희'	다른 대상이 여럿인 '그들/그것들'

Quick
Check-Up

Check the correct ones.

복수: we, you, they

A Look and choose.

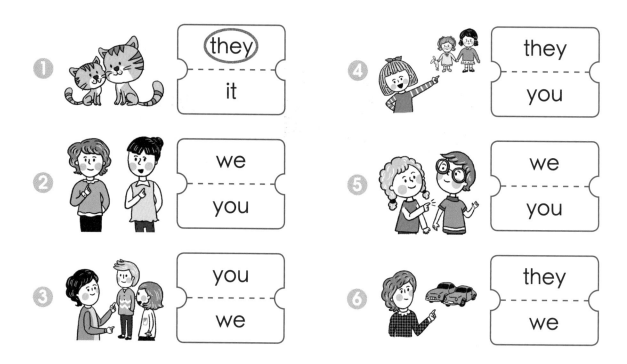

1. (they) / it
2. we / you
3. you / we
4. they / you
5. we / you
6. they / we

B Read and write.

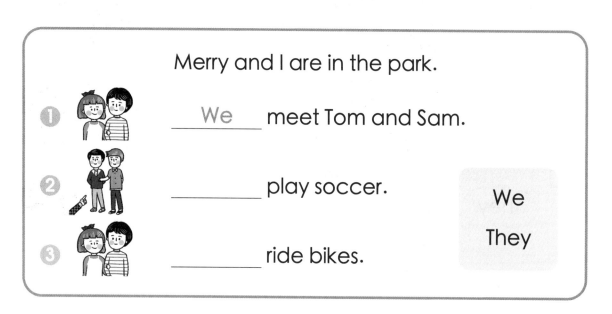

Merry and I are in the park.

1. ___We___ meet Tom and Sam.
2. _____ play soccer.
3. _____ ride bikes.

We
They

Trace and color.

주격 대명사, 목적격 대명사

주격 대명사

❀ 인칭대명사는 문장에서의 위치와 역할에 따라 모습과 의미가 달라져요.
주격 대명사는 주로 문장의 맨 앞에서 주어 역할을 해요.

	인칭	주격 (~은/는/이/가)
단수	1인칭	**I** 나는
	2인칭	**you** 너는
	3인칭	**he** 그는, **she** 그녀는, **it** 그것은
복수	1인칭	**we** 우리는
	2인칭	**you** 너희는
	3인칭	**they** 그들은/그것들은

Quick Check-Up — Circle the *subject pronouns.*

• subject pronoun 주격 대명사

① (I) like my bike.

② He likes apples.

③ They go home.

④ They can swim.

⑤ We play in the park.

⑥ They sing a song.

⑦ It is a cute pet.

⑧ He loves you.

주격 대명사

A Circle the *subject pronouns*.

① (We) have lunch together.   ③ They buy a bike.

② He likes cats.   ④ I like my white shirt.

B Complete the dialogues.

①
__You__ are at the party.
Yes, _____ am.

②
_____ is at the party.
_____ is also at the party.

③
_____ are at the party.
Yes, _____ are.

we	He
You	I	She

 Cut, choose, and put.

Subject Pronouns

he

※ 아래와 동일한 카드가 175쪽에 있습니다. 해당 페이지의 카드를 사용하세요.

he	boy	we	it	dog	hot
I	you	for	girl	she	they

Go to p. 175

목적격 대명사

❋ 인칭대명사의 목적격은 동사 다음에 위치해요.

	인칭	주격	목적격 (~을/를, ~에게)
단수	1인칭	I	**me** 나를
	2인칭	you	**you** 너를
	3인칭	he, she, it	**him** 그를, **her** 그녀를, **it** 그것을
복수	1인칭	we	**us** 우리를
	2인칭	you	**you** 너희를
	3인칭	they	**them** 그들을/그것들을

me

목적격 대명사는 보통
'~을/를, ~에게'로 해석해요.

Quick Check-Up Circle the *object pronouns.*   • object pronoun 목적격 대명사

❶ I like (him).

❷ He likes it.

❸ Tom loves us.

❹ She hates it.

❺ They love her.

❻ We like you.

❼ You call me.

❽ I see them.

A Read and match.

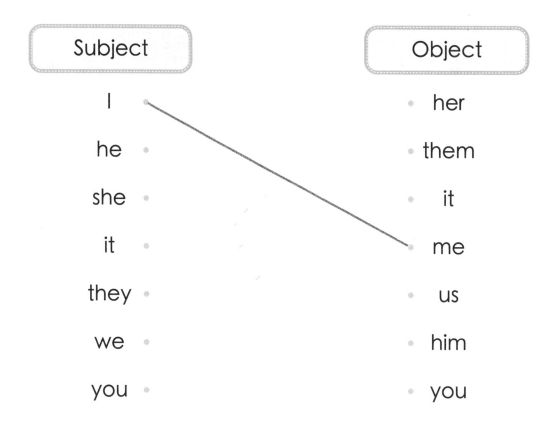

Subject	Object
I	her
he	them
she	it
it	me
they	us
we	him
you	you

B Read and write.

ex ___I___ see ___her___ , but ___she___ doesn't see ___me___ .

① I see him, but ___he___ doesn't see ___me___ .

② They see me, but _____ don't see _____ .

③ You see them, but _____ don't see _____ .

Color the hive.

Subject ▨ Object ▨

He is a student.

You are a good boy.

Tom gives **you** a book.

He wants books.

We are friends.

Judy calls **me**.

Jerry likes **us**.

Mom sends **me** a cake.

My sister likes **it**.

She loves **him**.

소유격

❀ '나의 ○○', '너의 ○○'와 같이 어떤 것이 누구의 것인지 나타내는 말을 '소유격'이라고 해요. [소유격+명사]의 형태로, 소유격은 항상 명사 앞에 위치해요.

He is **my** dad.
　　소유격 명사

They are **her** books.
　　　　소유격　　명사

	인칭	주격	목적격	소유격
단수	1인칭	I	me	**my** 나의
	2인칭	you	you	**your** 너의
	3인칭	he, she, it	him, her, it	**his** 그의, **her** 그녀의, **its** 그것의
복수	1인칭	we	us	**our** 우리의
	2인칭	you	you	**your** 너희들의
	3인칭	they	them	**their** 그들의

Quick Check-Up

Circle the *possessive adjectives*.

① I like (his) jacket.

② I love her house.

③ My shoes are old.

④ Our teacher is kind.

⑤ It is your shirt.

⑥ This is his bike.

⑦ Their car is black.

⑧ Its nose is big.

• possessive adjective 소유형용사, 소유격

소유격

A Read and match.

Subject Pronouns	Possessive Adjectives

Subject Pronouns:
I
you
he
she
it
we
they

Possessive Adjectives:
her
their
its
my
your
our
his

(I — my matched by line)

B Read and write.

1. It's ____her____ pen. (she)

2. It's _____ cat. (I)

3. It's _____ bag. (you)

4. It's _____ dog. (he)

5. These are _____ books. (they)

her
their
my
your
his

소유격

 Fun Wrap-Up! Look and write.

Kate   Tom   Paul   Ann

1. Tom, which is your bag?

   This is ____my____ bag.

2. Which is Ann's bag?

   This is _____ bag.

3. Which is Paul's bag?

   This is _____ bag.

4. Which is Kate's bag?

   This is _____ bag.

my
your
his
her
our
their

소유대명사

🌸 '~의 것'이라는 뜻으로 소유를 나타내는 말을 소유대명사라고 합니다.
소유대명사는 [소유격＋명사]의 역할을 해요.

Whose book is it?   Is this her book?

– It is **mine**(＝my book).   – Yes, it is **hers**(＝her book).

	인칭	주격	목적격	소유격	소유대명사
단수	1인칭	I	me	my	**mine** 나의 것
	2인칭	you	you	your	**yours** 너의 것
	3인칭	he, she, it	him, her, it	his, her, its	**his** 그의 것, **hers** 그녀의 것, ~~its~~
복수	1인칭	we	us	our	**ours** 우리들의 것
	2인칭	you	you	your	**yours** 너희들의 것
	3인칭	they	them	their	**theirs** 그들의 것

🌸 명사의 소유격과 소유대명사는 명사 뒤에 **'s**를 붙여 나타내요.

It is **Tom's** book.   The book is **Tom's**(＝Tom's book).
　　　소유격　　　　　　　　　　　　　　　　　　　　소유대명사

Quick Check-Up

Circle the correct ones.

hers (mine)	yours / ours	yours / ours	theirs / his	his / hers

A Read and match.

It is your gift.　　These are my books.　　This is her bike.

mine　　　his　　　hers　　　yours　　　theirs

He plays with his toys.　　It is their house.

B Complete the sentences with *possessive pronouns*.

1 This is **my book**.　　_____

2 It is **Tom's house**.　　_____

3 **Her shirt** is blue.　　Hers is blue.

4 They are **your socks**.　　_____

Cut and put.

It is _____ book.

This book is _____.

Possessive Adjectives

my

Possessive Pronouns

mine

※ 아래와 동일한 카드가 175쪽에 있습니다. 해당 페이지의 카드를 사용하세요.

its	his	yours	your	their
our	theirs	my	his	hers
mine	her	ours		

Go to p. 175

지시대명사

this, that

❀ 지시대명사는 사물이나 사람을 가리킬 때 사용해요. 가리키는 대상이
하나이면서 가까이 있으면 **this**, 멀리 있으면 **that**을 사용해요.

this	that
This is a pen.	**That** is a pen.
This is my brother.	**That** is my brother.

Quick Check-Up Complete the sentences with *this* or *that*.

① ___This___ is a banana.

③ _____ is an apple.

② _____ is a banana.

④ _____ is an apple.

this, that

A Look and circle.

1 (This)/ That is a bird.

2 This / That is an apple.

3 This / That is a car.

4 This / That is my teacher.

B Write *this* or *that*.

1

___This___ is a ball.

3

_____ is a house.

2
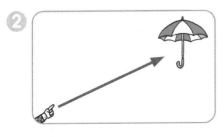
_____ is an umbrella.

4
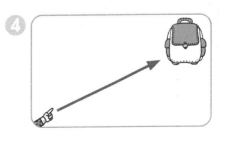
_____ is a bag.

 this, that

Fun Wrap-Up! Follow and circle.

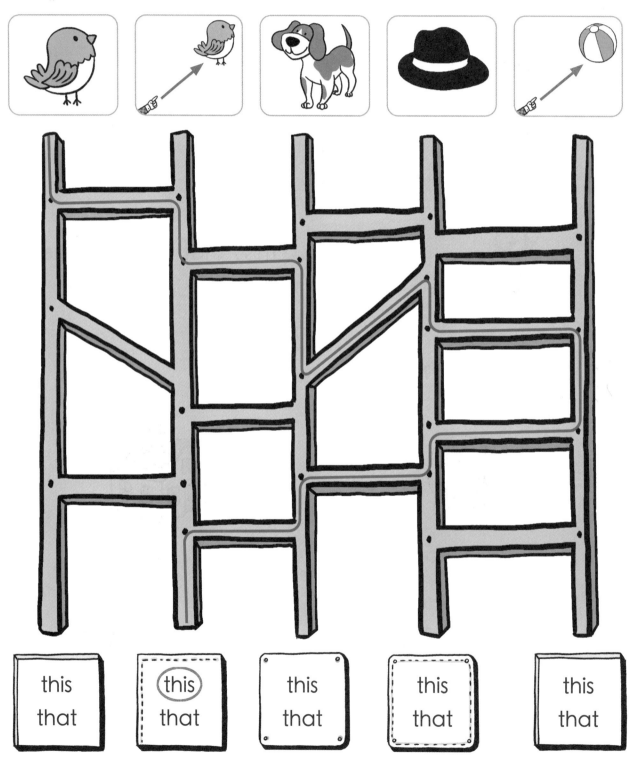

this	this	this	this	this
that	that	that	that	that

지시대명사

these, those

❋ 가리키는 대상이 여럿이고 가까이 있으면 these, 멀리 있으면 those를 사용해요.

this	these	that	those
This is an apple.	**These** are apples.	**That** is an apple.	**Those** are apples.
가까이 하나일 때 (이것, 이 사람)	가까이 여럿일 때 (이것들, 이 사람들)	멀리 하나일 때 (저것, 저 사람)	멀리 여럿일 때 (저것들, 저 사람들)

Quick Check-Up ## Circle the correct ones.

A Look and match.

1. this •
2. that •
3. these •
4. those •

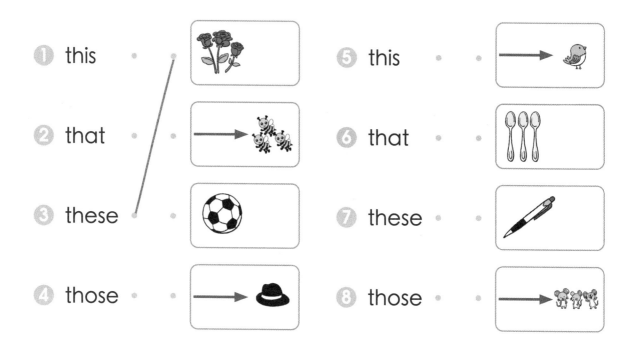

5. this • • 🐦
6. that • • 🥄🥄🥄
7. these • • 🖊
8. those • • 🐭🐭🐭

B Read and mark ○ or ✕.

1. This is a ball. ○

2. That is a tree. ☐

3. Those are bags. ☐

4. These are cats. ☐

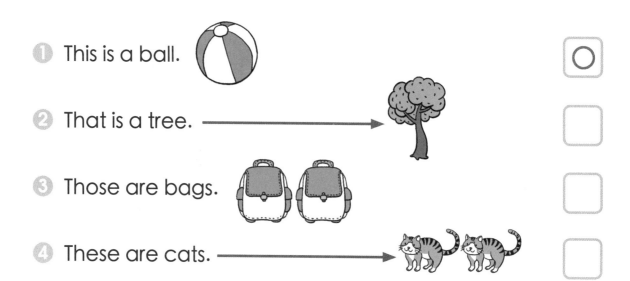

 Read and write.

Hello! I'm Lisa. _This_ is my cat.

_____ are my books.

_____ is my saxophone.

_____ are my parents.

_____ are my sisters.

| This | That |
| These | Those |

A Choose the correct answers.

1 I see him, but _____ doesn't see _____.

① you, we   ② he, me   ③ him, he

2 You see them, but _____ don't see _____.

① I, she   ② they, you   ③ You, I

3 Her shirt is blue. → _____ is blue.

① Hers   ② His   ③ Yours

4 It is Tom's house. → It is _____.

① mine   ② hers   ③ his

5 They are your socks. → They are _____.

① yours   ② theirs   ③ mine

B Fill in the blanks.

This	These	That	Those

1 _____ is a bird.

2 _____ is a tree.

3 _____ are cats.

4 _____ are bags.

C Unscramble the sentences.

1   meet / We / Tom and Sam.

_____

2   white shirt. / I / like / my

_____

3   their / are / books. / These

_____

4   my / Those / are / sisters.

_____

D Answer the questions.

1   What color is your shirt?

_____

2   Do you like that color?

_____

3   What color is your bag?

_____

4   What is your favorite color?

_____

Chapter

동사

3

I can do it!

주어의 인칭에 따른 변화

❋ '～(이)다' 또는 '～ 있다'라는 뜻을 지닌 동사를 'be동사'라고 해요.
be동사는 주어의 인칭에 따라 그 모습이 am, are, is로 달라지고,
줄여 쓰기도 해요.

	인칭	주어	be동사	축약형
단수	1인칭	I	**am**	I'**m**
	2인칭	You	**are**	You'**re**
	3인칭	He, She, It	**is**	He'**s**, She'**s**, It'**s**
복수	1인칭	We	**are**	We'**re**
	2인칭	You	**are**	You'**re**
	3인칭	They	**are**	They'**re**

Circle the correct ones.

① He   am / are / (is)

② She   am / are / is

③ I   am / are / is

④ It   am / are / is

⑤ You   am / are / is

⑥ We   am / are / is

⑦ They   am / are / is

A Check the correct sentences.

1. She are a girl. ☐
2. I am pretty. ☑
3. You're kind. ☐
4. We is friends. ☐
5. They're robots. ☐
6. I'm a singer. ☐
7. She is tall. ☐
8. He are happy. ☐
9. It are fun. ☐
10. We are family. ☐

B Correct and rewrite.

1. I **are** a girl.　　　I am a girl.

2. He **are** a doctor.　　_____

3. They **is** my friends.　_____

4. It **are** a cat.　　　_____

5. We **is** teachers.　　_____

 Fun Wrap-Up! Find the way to Finish.

Be동사

12

주어의 수에 따른 변화

⚙ be동사는 주어의 수에 따라서도 그 모습이 달라져요.

	주어	be동사	예문
단수	단수 명사 (A ball, A car, A house)	is	A ball/car/house **is** big.
	This, That, It		This **is** a car. That **is** blue. It **is** a bag.
복수	복수 명사 (Balls, Cars, Houses)	are	Balls/Cars/Houses **are** big.
	These, Those, They		These **are** my gifts. Those **are** trees. They **are** bags.

⚙ 주어가 물질명사이거나 추상명사일 때는 be동사 'is'를 써요.

Water **is** cold.　　　　　Love **is** sweet.

Quick Check-Up Check the correct ones.

☐ It is a book.　　　☐ Those are red.

☐ They are books.　　☐ A book are old.

☐ Jane are pretty.　　☐ These is bags.

☑ Water is cold.　　　☐ Love is sweet.

주어의 수에 따른 변화

A Read, choose, and write.

am	are	is

1. The balls _____ new.
2. The sky ___is___ blue.
3. It _____ long.
4. You _____ smart.
5. Lisa _____ kind.
6. Those _____ books.
7. They _____ sad.
8. She _____ brave.

B Fill in the blanks.

am	are	is

1. It ___is___ my birthday.
   My friends _____ at my party.
   They _____ happy.

2. You _____ happy today.
   These gifts _____ for you.
   The birthday party ___is___ so fun.

Fun Wrap-Up! Cut and put.

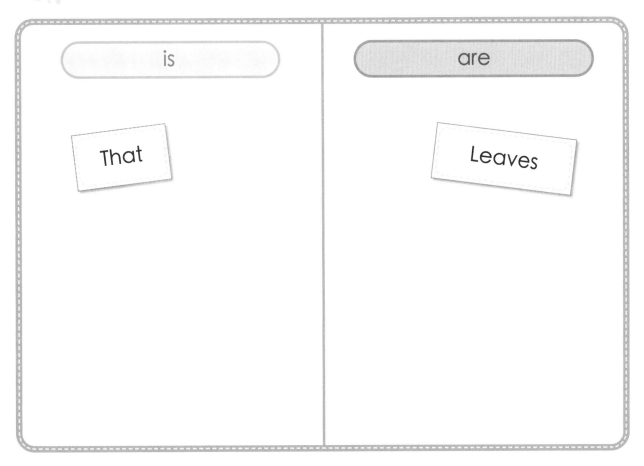

is	are
That	Leaves

※ 아래와 동일한 카드가 175쪽에 있습니다. 해당 페이지의 카드를 사용하세요.

That	Water	We	Love	Leaves	A book
A frog	These	Apples	Coffee	Tom and Jim	Those
He	This	Jim	She	The sky	It
Cats	Tom	They	A dog	Bees	A pig

Go to p. 175

Be동사: 부정문

am not, are not, is not

❀ '아니다' 또는 '없다' 같은 부정의 뜻을 가진 문장을 부정문이라고 해요.
be동사의 부정문은 be동사 뒤에 not을 넣으면 돼요.

	긍정문	부정문
단수	I am ~.	I am **not** ~.
	You are ~.	You are **not** ~.
	He is ~.	He is **not** ~.
	She is ~.	She is **not** ~.
	It is ~.	It is **not** ~.
복수	We are ~.	We are **not** ~.
	You are ~.	You are **not** ~.
	They are ~.	They are **not** ~.

Quick Check-Up — Check the correct ones.

☐ They not are hungry.　　☐ The king is not powerful.

☐ A banana not is red.　　☑ The pencil is not long.

☐ She is not kind.　　☐ We not are in the store.

☐ The baby is not cute.　　☐ He is not a doctor.

am not, are not, is not

A Change the sentences in the *negative forms*.

1. It is a dog. ➡ _It is not a dog._

2. You are students. ➡ _____

3. We are angels. ➡ _____

4. He is kind. ➡ _____

5. I am a writer. ➡ _____

B Complete the sentences in the *negative forms*.

1. I _____am not short_____. (short)

2. Math is _____. (easy)

3. She is _____. (sick)

4. They are _____. (girls)

5. You _____. (ugly)

6. We _____. (teachers)

am not, are not, is not

 Follow and match.

Tom is not tall.
Peter is tall.

We are not sad.
We are happy.

She is a singer.

I am not a queen.
I am a king.

They are angry.

Tom   Peter

Be동사: 부정문

aren't, isn't

❀ [be동사+not]은 다음과 같이 줄여 쓸 수도 있어요.

	긍정문	부정문	축약형
단수	I am ~.	I am **not** ~.	X
	You are ~.	You are **not** ~.	You **aren't** ~.
	He is ~.	He is **not** ~.	He **isn't** ~.
	She is ~.	She is **not** ~.	She **isn't** ~.
	It is ~.	It is **not** ~.	It **isn't** ~.
복수	We are ~.	We are **not** ~.	We **aren't** ~.
	You are ~.	You are **not** ~.	You **aren't** ~.
	They are ~.	They are **not** ~.	They **aren't** ~.

am not은 줄여 쓸 수 없어요.

Quick Check-Up

Write the correct *contraction* for the words.

❶ You are not tall.　　　　You aren't tall.

❷ He is not a singer.　　　_____

❸ Jane is not happy.　　　_____

❹ We are not angry.　　　_____

❺ Tom and Sam are not sad.　_____

• contraction 축약형

aren't, isn't

A Read and mark ○ or ✗.

1 She isn't a painter. ⬭⬭⬭⬭⬭⬭⬭⬭⬭⬭⬭⬭⬭⬭⬭⬭⬭⬭⬭⬭⬭⬭⬭⬭ ○

2 She isn't angry. ⬭⬭⬭⬭⬭⬭⬭⬭⬭⬭⬭⬭⬭⬭⬭⬭⬭⬭⬭⬭⬭⬭⬭⬭⬭⬭⬭⬭ ☐

3 They arenot nurses. ⬭⬭⬭⬭⬭⬭⬭⬭⬭⬭⬭⬭⬭⬭⬭⬭⬭⬭⬭⬭⬭ ☐

4 I amn't heavy. ⬭⬭⬭⬭⬭⬭⬭⬭⬭⬭⬭⬭⬭⬭⬭⬭⬭⬭⬭⬭⬭⬭⬭⬭⬭⬭⬭⬭⬭ ☐

5 These aren't my sisters. ⬭⬭⬭⬭⬭⬭⬭⬭⬭⬭⬭⬭⬭⬭⬭⬭⬭ ☐

B Fill in the blanks.

1 They _____aren't_____ students.

2 Sam _____ in the gym.

3 We _____ in London.

4 The dog _____ under the table.

5 I _____ in the country.

6 You _____ twelve years old.

7 She _____ a dancer.

| am not |
| aren't |
| isn't |

Match and color the boxes.

isn't ▨   aren't ▨

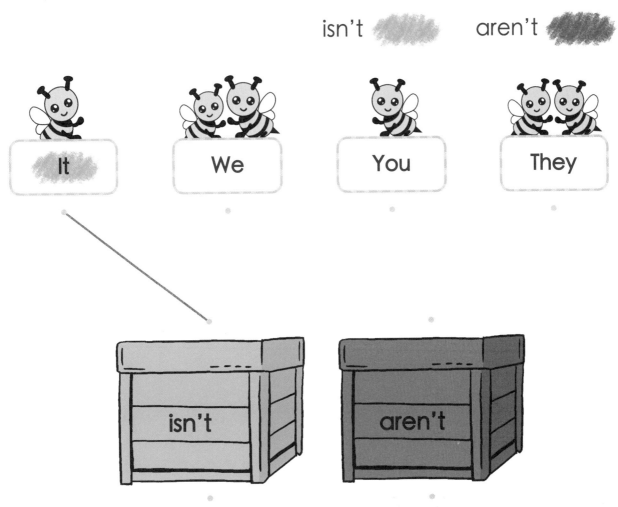

It   We   You   They

isn't   aren't

He   You   She

질문하기

❋ 무엇인가를 묻는 문장을 의문문이라고 해요. be동사의 의문문은 주어와 be동사의 위치를 바꿔서 만들고, 문장 끝에 물음표 **?** 를 찍어서 완성해요.

· **be**동사＋주어 ～?

She is strong .

Is she strong ?

They are friends .

Are they friends ?

	평서문	의문문
단수	I am ～.	Am I ～?
	You are ～.	Are you ～?
	He is ～.	Is he ～?
	She is ～.	Is she ～?
	It is ～.	Is it ～?
복수	We are ～.	Are we ～?
	You are ～.	Are you ～?
	They are ～.	Are they ～?

Quick Check-Up

Check the *asking sentences*.

· asking sentence 의문문

☐ I am ten years old.

☑ Are you strong?

☐ Are they your pencils?

☐ I am hungry.

☐ My pets are sweet.

☐ They are books.

☐ The baby is cute.

☐ Are you there?

 질문하기

A Fill in the blanks.

Am	Are	Is

① ___Is___ he a doctor?

② _____ you in the classroom?

③ _____ they friends?

④ _____ Lisa at home?

⑤ _____ that Nick?

B Complete the *asking sentences*.

I am 10 years old.
Jane is my best friend.
I am brave.

___Are you___ 10 years old?
_____ your best friend?
_____ brave?

Check the correct ones.

✓ Is she ~?	Are they ~?	Am I ~?	Are this ~?
Am you ~?	Are I ~?	Is she ~?	Are they ~?
Are they ~?	Is he ~?	Are you ~?	Is it ~?
Am I ~?	Are they ~?	Are she ~?	Are we ~?

Be동사: 의문문

대답하기

❋ be동사 의문문에 답할 때에는 질문에 대한 대답이 긍정일 때는
[Yes, 주어+be동사.], 부정일 때는 [No, 주어+be동사+not.]으로 답해요.

Are you a student?

- Yes, I am.

- No, I am not(=I'm not).

Is he a firefighter?

- Yes, he is.

- No, he is not(=isn't).

	의문문	긍정 대답	부정 대답
단수	Am I ~?	Yes, you are.	No, you are not(=aren't).
	Are you ~?	Yes, I am.	No, I am not(=I'm not).
	Is he ~?	Yes, he is.	No, he is not(=isn't).
	Is she ~?	Yes, she is.	No, she is not(=isn't).
	Is it ~?	Yes, it is.	No, it is not(=isn't).
복수	Are we ~?	Yes, you are.	No, you are not(=aren't).
	Are you ~?	Yes, we are.	No, we are not(=aren't).
	Are they ~?	Yes, they are.	No, they are not(=aren't).

1인칭 주어(I/we)와
2인칭 주어(You)로
물어볼 때는 인칭을
바꿔서 대답해요.

Quick Check-Up

Check the correct answers.

Sam   Tom

❶ Is Sam tall?
　☐ Yes, he is.　　☑ No, he isn't.

❷ Is Tom tall?
　☐ Yes, he is.　　☐ No, he isn't.

A Read and match.

1. Is he a doctor?
2. Are you hungry?
3. Are we smart?
4. Are they pencils?
5. Is it short?

- Yes, you are.
- No, they aren't.
- No, it isn't.
- No, I'm not.
- Yes, he is.

B Answer the questions.

Name: Lucy	Nationality: France
Age: 9	Job: student

Yes, she is.　　　　No, she isn't.

1. Is she Lucy?　　　　Yes, she is.

2. Is she nine years old?　　　　_____

3. Is she from France?　　　　_____

4. Is she a teacher?　　　　_____

Fun Wrap-Up! Answer the questions.

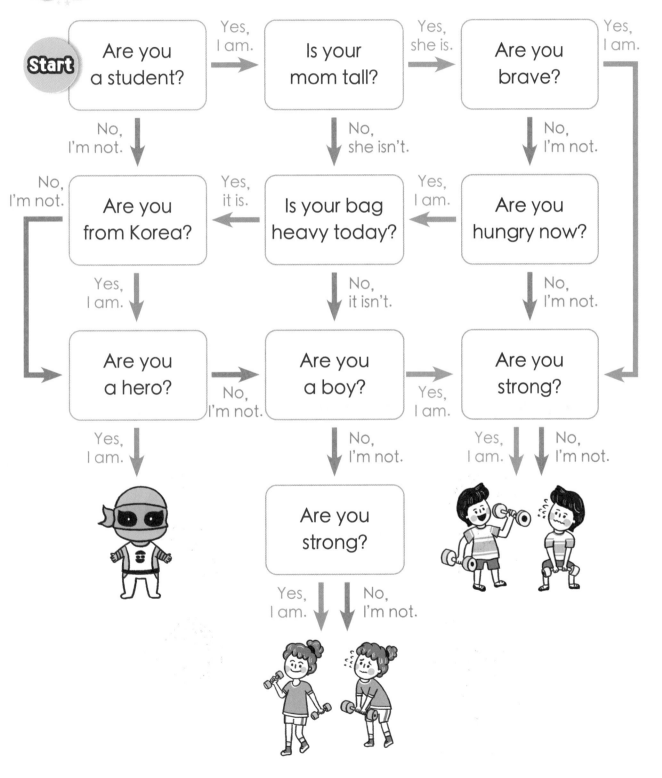

Start

Are you a student? — Yes, I am. → Is your mom tall? — Yes, she is. → Are you brave? — Yes, I am.

Are you a student? — No, I'm not. ↓

Is your mom tall? — No, she isn't. ↓

Are you brave? — No, I'm not. ↓

Are you from Korea? — No, I'm not.

Is your bag heavy today? — Yes, it is. ← Are you hungry now? — Yes, I am.

Are you hungry now? — No, I'm not. ↓

Are you from Korea? — Yes, I am. ↓

Is your bag heavy today? — No, it isn't. ↓

Are you a hero? — No, I'm not. → Are you a boy? — Yes, I am. → Are you strong?

Are you a hero? — Yes, I am. ↓

Are you a boy? — No, I'm not. ↓

Are you strong? — Yes, I am. / No, I'm not.

Are you strong? — Yes, I am. / No, I'm not.

일반동사

sing, drink, eat...

❀ 일반동사는 주어의 동작이나 상태를 나타내고, '~하다'라는 의미예요.
일반동사 현재형은 주어가 3인칭 단수인 경우를 제외하고, 동사원형을 그대로 써요.

I **sing** a song.
주어 동사원형

You **like** apples.
주어 동사원형

❀ 일반동사에는 다음과 같은 것들이 있어요.

talk 말하다	read 읽다	eat 먹다	drink 마시다
cry 울다	think 생각하다	sleep 자다	smile 미소 짓다

Quick Check-Up — Circle the correct ones.

① eat   talk
cry   (laugh)
think   drink

③ cry   sing
talk   sleep
smile   drink

② run   think
sing   read
eat   cry

④ eat   read
think   talk
run   drink

sing, drink, eat...

A Circle the *verbs*.

1. I (play) soccer.

2. They read books.

3. They eat bananas.

4. I drink water.

5. You sleep on the bed.

6. You have a ball.

7. I like English.

8. You go to school.

9. I dance.

10. They come home.

B Write the *verbs*.

play	she	read	sleep	he	like	run
here	talk	eat	red	come	drink	

_____play_____ _____ _____

_____ _____ _____

_____ _____ _____

sing, drink, eat...

TALK

WRITE

PLAY

READ

WALK

RUN

JUMP

W	R	U	N	W	W
A	P	A	J	A	R
L	L	J	U	M	I
K	A	K	M	K	T
P	Y	T	P	L	E
T	A	L	K	R	R
O	O	R	E	A	D

Lesson 15 일반동사

sings, drinks, eats...

🌸 일반동사는 주어에 따라 형태가 변해요. 주어가 3인칭 단수이고
현재 시제일 경우에는 대부분의 일반동사 뒤에 -(e)s를 붙여요.

대부분의 동사	-s	run → run**s** eat → eat**s** buy → buy**s** come → come**s**
자음+y로 끝나는 동사	-y → -ies	study → stud**ies** try → tr**ies** carry → carr**ies** fly → fl**ies**
-o, -x, -s, -sh, -ch로 끝나는 동사	-es	go → go**es** fix → fix**es** pass → pass**es** wash → wash**es** teach → teach**es**

 Quick Check-Up ── Circle the correct ones.

① I drink / drinks water.　⑥ They read / reads books.

② You sing / sings .　⑦ He teach / teaches Math.

③ She cry / cries .　⑧ They cook / cooks pasta.

④ He swim / swims .　⑨ She wash / washes a car.

⑤ I work / works .　⑩ He sleep / sleeps .

sings, drinks, eats...

A Read, circle, and write.

1. It ___sounds___ great.   sound / (sounds)

2. I _____ TV.   watch / watches

3. He _____ coffee.   drink / drinks

4. A monkey _____ up a tree.   climb / climbs

5. A rose _____ sweet.   smell / smells

B Correct and rewrite.

1. He ~~run~~ fast.   He runs fast.

2. She **watch** the movie.   _____

3. He **write** a letter.   _____

4. She **like** to read books.   _____

5. The baby **cry**.   _____

Color the leaves with the right sentences.

I eats
an apple.

Dad swims.

She write a letter.

He rides a bike.

They smiles.

You see
the bird.

I swim.

일반동사: 부정문

do not[don't]

✿ 일반동사를 부정문으로 만들 때는 동사 앞에 do not/does not을 넣어요.
주어가 1인칭, 2인칭, 또는 3인칭 복수일 때는 [주어＋do not＋동사원형]
형태를 써요.

인칭		일반동사 부정문
I	1인칭 단수	
we	1인칭 복수	**do not**(=**don't**)＋동사원형
you	2인칭 단수, 복수	
they	3인칭 복수	

I ride a bike. → I **do not**(=**don't**) ride a bike.

We cry. → We **do not**(=**don't**) cry.

You eat pizza. → You **do not**(=**don't**) eat pizza.

They swim fast. → They **do not**(=**don't**) swim fast.

Quick
Check-Up
Check the correct *negative forms*. •negative form 부정형

☑ I do not cry.　　　　☐ I does not eat pizza.

☐ They don't swim.　　☐ They doesn't jump.

☐ You doesn't smile.　　☐ You don't run.

☐ We do not walk.　　　☐ We does not sleep.

do not [don't]

A **Complete the sentences in the *negative forms*.**

① You _____don't have_____ a ball. (have)

② They _____ books. (read)

③ We _____ . (cry)

④ I _____ the piano. (play)

⑤ I _____ TV. (watch)

B **Unscramble the sentences.**

① do not / swim. / We _____We do not swim._____

② They / smile. / do not _____

③ like / pizza. / do not / I _____

④ I / drink / do not / water. _____

⑤ run. / do not / You _____

 do not[don't]

 Fun Wrap-Up! Follow and circle.

I don't run. | I don't jump. | I eat pizza. | I don't swim.

일반동사: 부정문

does not[doesn't]

❋ 주어가 3인칭 단수이고 현재 시제일 때 일반동사의 부정문은
[주어＋does not＋동사원형] 형태로 만들어요.

He runs.

→ He **does not** run.

(＝He **doesn't** run.)

She cooks pasta.

→ She **does not** cook pasta.

(＝She **doesn't** cook pasta.)

Quick Check-Up — Check the correct ones.

☑ It doesn't rain.

☐ He does not speaks English well.

☐ My dog does not run fast.

☐ She do not eat hamburgers.

☐ The boy does not play baseball.

☐ She doesn't cleans her room.

does not[doesn't]

A Circle the correct ones.

1. My friend (does not) do not like chocolate.

2. He does not / do not make a boat.

3. She does not / do not teach Korean.

4. Judy does not / do not dance.

5. Tom does not / do not drink coffee.

6. The man does not / do not go shopping.

B Complete the sentence in the *negative form*.

1. He ___doesn't___ ___drive___ a car. (drive)

2. She _____ _____ to music. (listen)

3. Mom _____ _____. (move)

4. A snake _____ _____. (walk)

5. Tom _____ _____ math. (study)

Follow the correct sentences.

He don't run.

He doesn't run.

She don't cry.

I don't cry.

She don't swim.

She doesn't swim.

I doesn't sleep. I don't sleep.

We doesn't study.

일반동사: 의문문

질문하기

❀ 일반동사 의문문은 문장 맨 앞에 **Do/Does**를 넣어서 만들어요.
주어가 <u>1인칭</u>, <u>2인칭</u>, 또는 <u>3인칭 복수</u>일 때는 [Do+주어+동사원형 ~?]
형태를 써요.

I **like** apples. → **Do you like** apples?

❀ 주어가 <u>3인칭 단수</u>이고 <u>현재</u>일 때는 [Does+주어+동사원형 ~?] 형태를
써요. 이때 주어 다음에 나오는 동사는 꼭 동사원형을 써야 해요.

She has lunch. → **Does she have** lunch? (○)
　　　　　　 → **Does she has** lunch? (✕)

Quick Check-Up **Circle the correct ones.**

❶
(Does) / Do
she run fast?

❸
Does / Do
they dance?

❷
Does / Do
she draw?

❹
Does / Do
you watch TV?

A Change the sentences into the *asking sentences*.

1. You run fast. ➡ _____Do you_____ run fast?

2. He buys a cake. ➡ _____ a cake?

3. She sleeps. ➡ _____ sleep?

4. They play tennis. ➡ _____ play tennis?

5. They watch TV. ➡ _____ watch TV?

B Correct and rewrite the sentences.

1. **Does** they go to school? _____

2. ~~Do~~ she ~~likes~~ oranges? Does she like oranges?

3. **Does** you drink milk? _____

4. Does he **plays** baseball? _____

5. **Does** we have a pen? _____

6. **Do** she hurt her leg? _____

 Follow and ask.

Do you read a book?

Does he cry?

Does she listen to music?

대답하기

❋ 일반동사 의문문에 대답할 때에는 아래와 같이 말해요.

Do you like orange juice?

– Yes, I do.

– No, I don't(=do not).

❋ 주어가 3인칭 단수일 때는 다음과 같이 대답해요.

Does she like orange juice?

– Yes, she does.

– No, she doesn't(=does not).

❋ 주어는 항상 대명사로 바꿔요.

Does John like math?

– Yes, **he** does.

John ⸻ he

Quick
Check-Up

Check the correct ones.

☐ Yes, I does. ☑ Yes, he does.

☐ No, she don't. ☐ No, they doesn't.

☐ Yes, she does. ☐ Yes, Tom do.

☐ No, we don't. ☐ No, I do.

A Read and write.

1. Do you like soccer? — Yes, I ____do____ .

2. Does Tom study math? — Yes, he _____ .

3. Do they sing? — No, they _____ .

4. Does he jump? — No, he _____ .

5. Does your sister sleep? — Yes, she _____ .

6. Do you play the piano? — No, I _____ .

B Unscramble the sentences.

1. work? / Does / he   Does he work?

2. he / No, / doesn't.   _____

3. you / like / Do / carrots? _____

4. I / do. / Yes,   _____

5. Does / write / she / a letter? _____

Follow and answer.

Does she swim?

Does he play basketball?

Do they run?

Does he eat apples?

No, he doesn't.

Yes, they do.

Yes, she does.

No, he doesn't.

Basic Test

A Choose the correct answers.

1 I _____ a girl.

   ① is   ② am   ③ are

2 You _____ kind.

   ① are   ② is   ③ am

3 She _____ sick.

   ① are not   ② am not   ③ is not

4 These _____ my sisters.

   ① isn't   ② aren't   ③ am not

5 Are you hungry? - _____

   ① No, I'm not.   ② Yes, he is.   ③ No, I amnot.

B Fill in the blanks.

does	teaches	sleep	Does	does not

1 You _____ on the bed.

2 He _____ math.

3 The boy _____ play baseball.

4 _____ she hurt her leg? - Yes, she _____.

C Unscramble the sentences.

1 gifts / are / These / for you.

_____

2 is / easy. / not / Math

_____

3 under / The dog / isn't / the table.

_____

4 the classroom? / you / Are / in

_____

D Answer the questions.

1 Are you strong?

_____

2 Do you study English?

_____

3 Are you 9 years old?

_____

4 Do you like pizza?

_____

Chapter

형용사 ①

4

I can do it!

형용사란?

❋ 형용사는 명사 앞에서 명사를 꾸며 주거나 동사 뒤에서 주어의 상태를 설명해 주는 역할을 해요.

I have a cat. → I have a **cute** cat.
형용사

❋ 형용사는 주로 사물의 색깔, 크기, 상태나 생김새 등을 나타내요.

색깔	red, blue, black, yellow, green
크기, 모양	big, small, tall, short, round, square
성격, 맛, 기분, 상태	kind, pretty, happy, sad, quiet, hungry, full, good, bad, sweet, sour, clean, dirty, soft
날씨	hot, cold, sunny, cloudy, cool

Quick Check-Up — Circle the correct *adjectives*.

• adjective 형용사

❶  happy / (sad)

❸  sunny / cloudy

❷  clean / dirty

❹  round / square

형용사란?

A Find and circle the *adjectives*.

1. I have a (cute) dog.

2. She has short hair.

3. He is a kind boy.

4. Judy is a good student.

5. I drink cold water.

6. I am hungry.

7. They are nice people.

8. This is a new book.

9. It is a blue desk.

10. We have a big bag.

B Read and match.

1. Elephants are   sunny.

2. Candies are   fast.

3. Giraffes are   big.

4. It is   sweet.

5. Trains are   tall.

 Follow, choose, and circle.

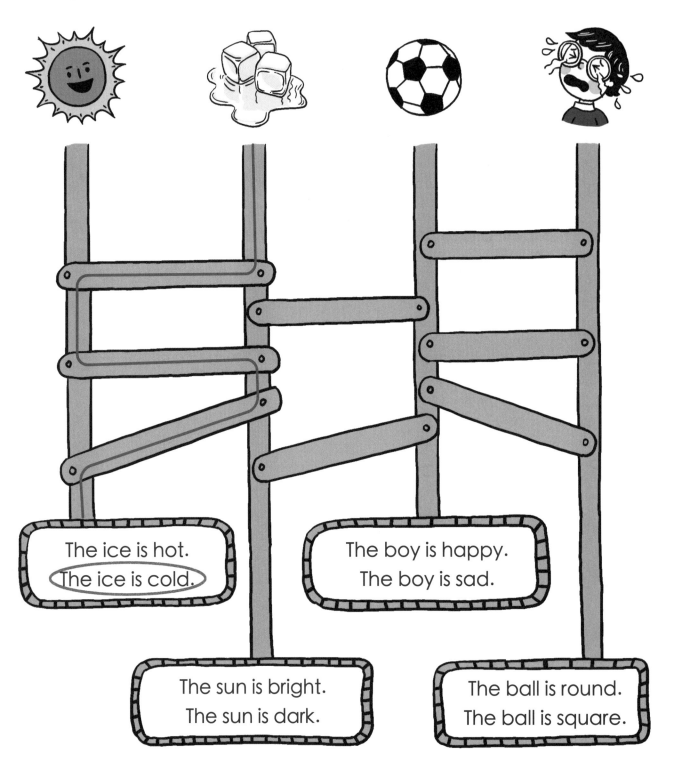

The ice is hot.
(The ice is cold.)

The boy is happy.
The boy is sad.

The sun is bright.
The sun is dark.

The ball is round.
The ball is square.

형용사의 위치

⚘ 형용사는 관사(a, an, the)나 소유격(my, your, his) 뒤에서 명사를 설명하거나 부사 뒤에 와요.

He is **a tall** man.   It is **a round** table.

It's **her new** dress.   Look at **her happy** face.

They are **very good** friends.   These are **very good** shoes.

⚘ 형용사는 be동사의 뒤에서 주어를 설명해 주는 역할을 해요.

He is **tall**.   The table is **round**.

She is **happy**.   The room is **small**.

 Circle the correct ones.

① small my phone / ⟨my small phone⟩

② a round table / round a table

③ her face happy / her happy face

④ very shoes good / very good shoes

⑤ his new book / book new his

형용사의 위치

A Write the best word to finish the sentence.

1. I have a _____short_____ pencil. | (short)/ slow |

2. They are very _____ students. | round / good |

3. My classroom is _____ . | clean / kind |

4. Dogs are _____ . | cute / sunny |

5. My mom's car is _____ . | hungry / new |

B Unscramble the sentences.

1. My bike / old. / is   _My bike is old._

2. tall. / Her brother / is   _____

3. water. / cold / This is / very   _____

4. black. / is / Your pen   _____

5. I / blue / pants. / have   _____

6. has / She / good / a / pen.   _____

Read and draw.

She has long hair.

My bag is green.

The man is tall.

The table is round.

This, That

지시형용사

🌸 지시형용사 this, that은 뒤에 있는 명사를 꾸며 주는 역할을 해요.
명사가 가까이 있는지 멀리 있는지, 단수인지 복수인지에 따라 다음과 같이
사용해요.

	가까이	멀리
단수	**this** book 이 책	**that** book 저 책
복수	**these** books 이 책들	**those** books 저 책들

This pen is mine.   **That** pen is mine.

These pens are mine.   **Those** pens are mine.

Quick
Check-Up

Circle the correct ones.

①
this ball
(these balls)

③
this mouse
these mice

②
that car
those cars

④
that flower
those flowers

지시형용사

A Circle the correct ones.

1. **(this)** / these | pencil
2. that / those | houses
3. this / these | books
4. that / those | flower
5. this / these | apples

6. that / those | oranges
7. this / these | girl
8. that / those | rulers
9. this / these | man
10. that / those | building

B Change the sentences.

1. This cat is cute. ➡ _____These cats_____ are cute.

2. That building is tall. ➡ _____ are tall.

3. This house is nice. ➡ _____ are nice.

4. That dog is black. ➡ _____ are black.

5. This bird is small. ➡ _____ are small.

6. That ruler is long. ➡ _____.

Fun Wrap-Up! Fill in the blanks with *this, that, these,* or *those*.

Those mountains are very high!

_____ island is too far away.

_____ birds are very hungry.

Stay away from _____ dog!

This, That

지시대명사

✿ this, that, these, those는 지시대명사로도 사용돼요.

지시형용사	지시대명사
This bag is yours. 이 가방은	**This** is your bag. 이것은
These bags are yours. 이 가방들은	**These** are your bags. 이것들은
That bag is yours. 저 가방은	**That** is your bag. 저것은
Those bags are yours. 저 가방들은	**Those** are your bags. 저것들은

Quick Check-Up

Circle the correct ones.

① This is your clock.

→ This clock / These clock   is yours.

② That is my book.

→ Those book / That book   is mine.

③ These are white dogs.

→ Those dogs / These dogs   are white.

지시대명사

A Change the sentences.

1. This is my pen. ➡ _This pen_ is mine.

2. Those are nice hats. ➡ _____ are nice.

3. These are old books. ➡ _____ are old.

4. That is a new eraser. ➡ _____ is new.

5. This is a fast car. ➡ _____ is fast.

B Look and match.

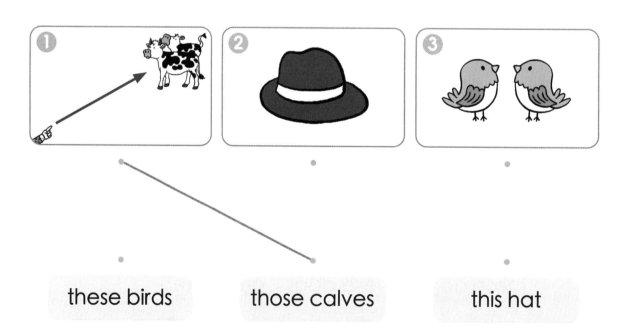

these birds   those calves   this hat

Read and color.

1. That sun is yellow.

2. This tree is green.

3. Those balls are blue.

4. These flowers are orange.

수량형용사 1

many, much, a lot of

❀ 어떤 것의 수나 양을 나타내는 말을 수량형용사라고 해요.

many, much, a lot of는 '많은'이라는 뜻으로, 뒤에 나오는 명사의
종류에 따라 다음과 같이 사용해요.

셀 수 있는 명사	**many**	수가 많은	**many** books
셀 수 없는 명사	**much**	양이 많은	**much** milk
셀 수 있는 명사 셀 수 없는 명사	**a lot of**	수, 양이 많은	**a lot of** books **a lot of** milk

❀ a lot of는 lots of로 바꿔 쓸 수 있어요.

lots of(=a lot of) books   **lots of**(=a lot of) milk

Quick Check-Up — Circle the correct ones.

❶ many water
(much water)

❸ a lot of balls
much balls

❷ many hats
much hats

❹ many flour
a lot of flour

many, much, a lot of

A Circle the correct ones.

1. (many)/ much pens
2. many / much water
3. many / much boys
4. many / much books

5. many / much juice
6. many / much sugar
7. many / much toys
8. many / much rulers

B Correct and rewrite the sentences.

1. I have **many** juice.   I have much juice.

2. They have **much** hats.   _____

3. He has **much** friends.   _____

4. My uncle has **much** dogs.   _____

5. We have **much** cups.   _____

6. I have **much** pencils.   _____

many, much, a lot of

 Choose and number.

1 We have (many)/ much apples.  ☐

2 I drink many / much water.  ☐

3 My son eats many / much yogurt.  1

4 She has many / much toys.  ☐

5 We need many / much bread.   ☐

6 He has many / much friends.  ☐

수량형용사 1

few, a few, little, a little

✿ a few, a little은 수나 양이 조금 있을 때 '조금 있는'이라는 의미로 쓰이고, few, little은 수나 양이 거의 없을 때 '거의 없는'이라는 뜻으로 사용해요.

• 셀 수 있는 명사

a few	조금 있는, 몇몇의	I have **a few** apples.
few	거의 없는	I have **few** apples.

• 셀 수 없는 명사

a little	조금 있는	I have **a little** water.
little	거의 없는	I have **little** water.

Quick Check-Up — Check the correct ones.

☐ a little people   ☑ a few people

☐ few money   ☐ few dogs

☐ little coke   ☐ little desks

☐ a few apples   ☐ a little animals

☐ a few balls   ☐ a little balls

few, a few, little, a little

A Circle the correct ones.

1. (a few)/ a little eggs
2. few / little time
3. a few / a little candies
4. few / little coffee
5. a few / a little students
6. few / little butter
7. a few / a little clothes
8. few / little tea

B Look and match.

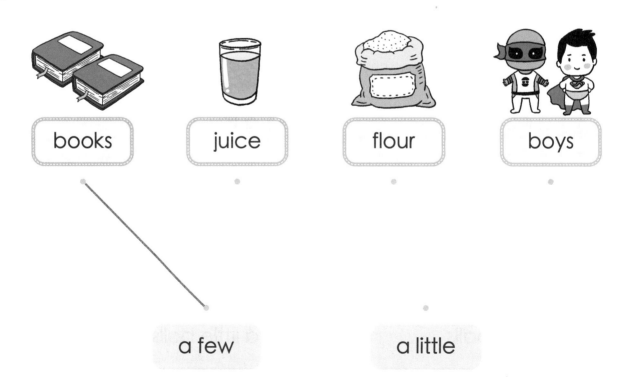

books

juice

flour

boys

a few

a little

Color the rainbow.

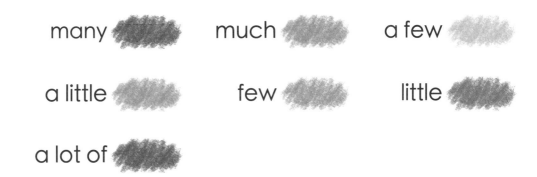

many   much   a few

a little   few   little

a lot of

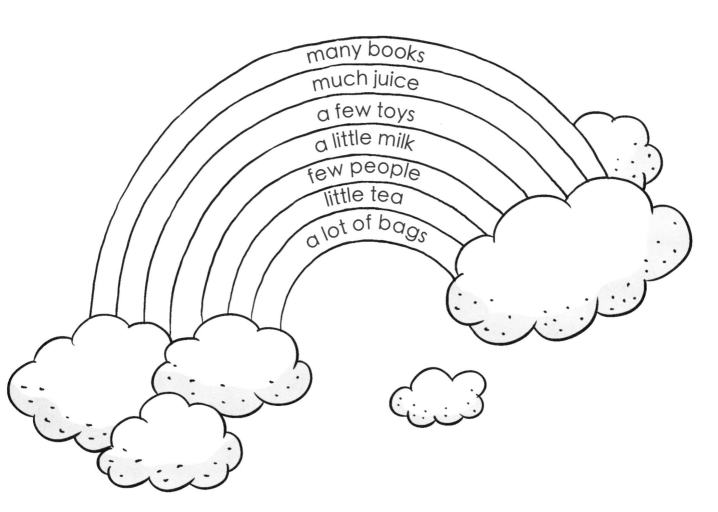

many books
much juice
a few toys
a little *milk*
few people
little tea
a lot of bags

수량형용사 2

some, any

❋ some, any는 '어느 정도의, 약간의'라는 뜻으로 정해지지 않은 수량을 나타내요. some, any는 문장의 종류에 따라 아래와 같이 사용해요.

some	주로 긍정문	약간의, 어느 정도의
any	주로 부정문	조금도, 전혀
	주로 의문문	약간의 ~도

I have **some** notebooks.

I don't have **any** money.

Do you have **any** candies?

some과 any는 셀 수 있는 명사와 셀 수 없는 명사 앞에 모두 쓸 수 있어요.

❋ some은 의문문에 쓰여 '요청, 부탁, 권유'를 나타내기도 해요.

Can I have **some** juice?

Quick Check-Up Complete the sentences with *some* or *any*.

❶ I have ___some___ juice.

❷ We don't have _____ cats.

❸ Do you have _____ candies?

❹ She has _____ pants.

some, any

A Circle the correct ones.

1. I have ((some)/ any) bananas.

2. We need (some / any) milk.

3. Do you have (some / any) questions?

4. I don't have (some / any) candies.

5. I make (some / any) bread.

B Read and mark ○ or ✕.

1. We don't have some soup. —— ✕

2. I don't need some water. ☐

3. Do you have any sisters? ☐

4. I don't have some friends. ☐

5. I have some bags in my room. ☐

some, any

Follow the word *some*.

수량형용사 2

every, all

* every, all은 둘 다 '모든'의 의미로 [every+단수 명사], [all+복수 명사]의 형태로 쓰여요.

- every + 단수 명사

Every child needs love.   **Every man** is busy.

- all + 복수 명사

All students eat lunch.   **All fruits** are fresh.

Quick Check-Up

Circle the correct ones.

① (All)/ Every   boys are hungry.

② All / Every   boy is hungry.

③ All / Every   child is sad.

④ All / Every   children are sad.

⑤ All / Every   books are interesting.

⑥ All / Every   book is interesting.

⑦ All / Every   flowers are pretty.

⑧ All / Every   flower is pretty.

All
+ 복수 명사

Every
+ 단수 명사

every, all

A **Fill in the blanks.**

all / All	every / Every

1 ___All___ the boys are students.

2 She likes _____ kinds of movies.

3 _____ house has a door.

4 _____ children go to school.

5 I play the piano _____ day.

B **Look and change the sentences.**

1 All animals sleep. ➔ _Every animal sleeps._

2 All roses are red. ➔ _____

3 All horses have four legs. ➔ _____

4 All cars are clean. ➔ _____

5 All trains are long. ➔ _____

Find the words in the puzzle.

E	A	N	Y	V
S	L	V	T	U
O	L	E	Y	T
M	Y	E	R	Y
E	M	A	N	Y

ALL   SOME   ANY   MANY

A **Choose the correct answers.**

1 Look at _____ face.

① her happy   ② happy her   ③ she happy

2 _____ are cute.

① This cats   ② That cat   ③ These cats

3 He has _____ friends.

① a   ② many   ③ much

4 I have _____ apples.

① much   ② a few   ③ little

5 I have _____ water.

① little   ② few   ③ a few

B **Fill in the blanks.**

All	Every	some	any

1 I don't have _____ money.

2 I have _____ juice.

3 _____ man is busy.

4 _____ students eat lunch.

C Unscramble the sentences.

1 people. / are / They / nice

_____

2 birds / Those / small. / are

_____

3 have / many / I / pencils.

_____

4 good / are / very / These / shoes.

_____

D Answer the questions.

1 How many erasers do you have?

_____

2 Do you have short hair or long hair?

_____

3 Do you have any sisters?

_____

4 Do you have any red pants?

_____

MEMO

Answers

문장의 특징

Quick Check-Up p. 6

☑ I like my bike.　☐ I like my bike

☐ play in the park.　☑ We play in the park.

☐ to school　☑ I go to school.

☑ The baby can speak.　☐ the baby can speak.

☑ Mom is in the store.　☐ Mom is in the store

A p. 7

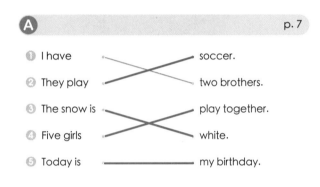

1. I have — two brothers.
2. They play — play together.
3. The snow is — white.
4. Five girls — soccer.
5. Today is — my birthday.

B p. 7

1. we are friends.　We are friends.
2. it is a dog.　It is a dog.
3. You are kind　You are kind.
4. the boys play games.　The boys play games.
5. I love my mom,　I love my mom.
6. The sun is bright　The sun is bright.

Fun Wrap-Up! p. 8

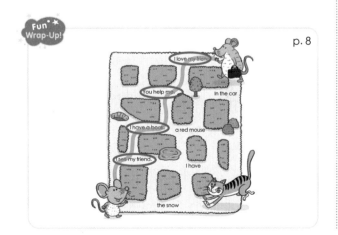

I love my friend.
You help me.
In the car
I have a book.
a red mouse
I see my friend.
I have
the snow

문장의 종류

Quick Check-Up p. 9

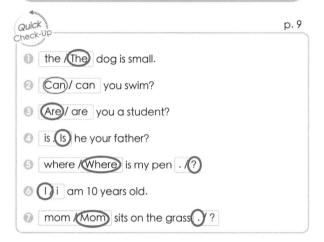

1. the / The dog is small.
2. Can / can you swim?
3. Are / are you a student?
4. is / Is he your father?
5. where / Where is my pen . / ?
6. I / i am 10 years old.
7. mom / Mom sits on the grass . / ?

A p. 10

1. I can run　✗
2. My dog is small.　O
3. i am tall.　✗
4. What is your name.　✗
5. Where are you?　O

B p. 10

1. he can run fast.　He can run fast.
2. are you cold?　Are you cold?
3. they are thirsty.　They are thirsty.
4. can you dance?　Can you dance?
5. is it a chair?　Is it a chair?
6. I am hungry.　I am hungry.

Fun Wrap-Up! p. 11

They are tired.
Is she Anne?
I am a student.
Are they teachers?
She is happy.
Is it a car?
How beautiful!

명사란?

Quick Check-Up p. 12

☑ house ☑ dog ☑ park ☑ bag
☑ pen ☐ go ☑ bird ☐ is
☑ teacher ☐ in ☐ of ☑ market
☐ see ☑ school ☐ come ☐ eat
☑ car ☑ hat ☑ mouse ☑ girl

a / an + 단수명사

Quick Check-Up p. 15

① (a) / an dog   ⑥ (a) / an rabbit
② a / (an) orange   ⑦ a / (an) umbrella
③ (a) / an banana   ⑧ (a) / an boy
④ (a) / an girl   ⑨ a / (an) egg
⑤ a / (an) ox   ⑩ (a) / an watermelon

A p. 13

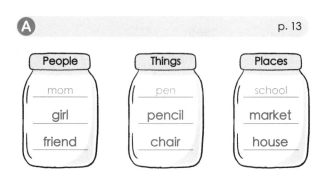

People	Things	Places
mom	pen	school
girl	pencil	market
friend	chair	house

A p. 16

① I have a apple. ──────── ✕
② I buy an eraser. ──────── ◯
③ She eats a orange. ──────── ✕
④ I need a umbrella. ──────── ✕
⑤ I want a cat. ──────── ◯

B p. 13

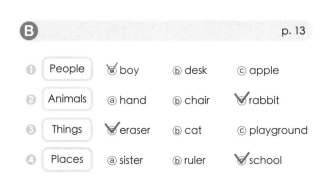

① People ☑ⓐ boy ⓑ desk ⓒ apple
② Animals ⓐ hand ⓑ chair ☑ⓒ rabbit
③ Things ☑ⓐ eraser ⓑ cat ⓒ playground
④ Places ⓐ sister ⓑ ruler ☑ⓒ school

B p. 16

① I am __a__ student.
② I have __an__ egg.
③ I need __a__ toy car.
④ Tom sees __an__ ant.
⑤ They want __a__ watermelon.

(a / an matching lines) a / an

Fun Wrap-Up! p. 14

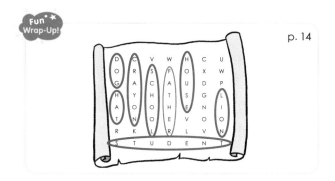

Fun Wrap-Up! a ▨ an ▨ p. 17

셀 수 있는 명사

명사의 복수형: 규칙

Quick Check-Up p. 18

1. box — boxs / (boxes)
2. tomato — tomatos / (tomatoes)
3. school — (schools) / schooles
4. radio — (radios) / radioes
5. wolf — wolfes / (wolves)

A p. 19

-s	-es	-ies	-ves
1. pear **pears**	1. bus **buses**	1. berry berries	1. half **halves**
2. note **notes**	2. dish **dishes**	2. baby **babies**	2. wolf **wolves**
3. girl **girls**	3. watch **watches**	3. lady **ladies**	3. shelf **shelves**

B p. 19

1. I wash the dishs. ✕
2. My mom tells us many stories. ○
3. Knifes are dangerous. ✕
4. Here come two buses. ○
5. She has two babys. ✕

Fun Wrap-Up! p. 20

1. How many blocks did you color? **10**
2. What letter did you make? **u(U)**

명사의 복수형: 불규칙

Quick Check-Up p. 21

foot → feet
children → singular / child
tooth → teeth
people → plural
goose → person / geese

A p. 22

1. I have 24 **teeth** .
2. There are five **children** in the room.
3. My **feet** are painful after walking.
4. I see many **geese** in the lake.
5. The cat chases three **mice** .

B p. 22

1. I wear a glass. — glasses
2. I have some pant. — pants
3. We have many box. — boxes
4. Childs love toys. — Children
5. I need a scissor. — scissors

Fun Wrap-Up! p. 23

고유명사

Quick Check-Up   p. 24

☑ Mr. Lee ☐ mrs. smith ☑ Mike ☐ Koreas

☐ paris ☑ Sunday ☐ america ☑ Christmas

☐ a Monday ☑ May ☑ Seoul ☑ Friday

☐ labor day ☑ July ☐ busan ☑ August

A   p. 25

1. My name is amily. ___Amily___
2. It is a Tuesday. ___Tuesday___
3. Yesterday was may 2. ___May___
4. Today is children's day. ___Children's Day___
5. They are from japan. ___Japan___

B   p. 25

1. My mom's birthday is in ___February___.
2. My uncle lives in ___Seoul___.
3. The party is on ___Saturday___.
4. His name is ___David___.
5. We sing carols at ___Christmas___.

Answers vary.

Fun Wrap-Up!   p. 26

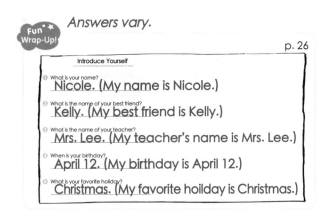

Introduce Yourself

1. What is your name?
   Nicole. (My name is Nicole.)
2. What is the name of your best friend?
   Kelly. (My best friend is Kelly.)
3. What is the name of your teacher?
   Mrs. Lee. (My teacher's name is Mrs. Lee.)
4. When is your birthday?
   April 12. (My birthday is April 12.)
5. What is your favorite holiday?
   Christmas. (My favorite hoilday is Christmas.)

물질명사, 추상명사

Quick Check-Up   p. 27

☑ millk ☑ love ☑ salt ☑ hope

☐ people ☐ a chair ☑ snow ☑ oil

☑ English ☑ bread ☑ time ☐ a car

☑ coffee ☐ pants ☑ water ☐ cats

☐ a pen ☑ art ☐ schools ☐ a boy

A   p. 28

1. I listen to music. ○
2. I buy two sugars. ✕
3. We have water. ○
4. They have good friendships. ✕
5. I put a rice in the pot. ✕
6. I have two coffees. ✕

B   p. 28

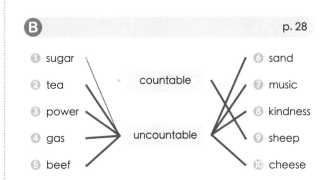

1. sugar
2. tea
3. power
4. gas
5. beef

countable

uncountable

6. sand
7. music
8. kindness
9. sheep
10. cheese

Fun Wrap-Up!   p. 29

단수

p. 30

Quick Check-Up

1. a (glass) / bag of water
2. a (can) / piece of coke
3. a bowl / (loaf) of bread
4. a (cup) / bag of coffee
5. a (sheet) / bowl of paper
6. a (bowl) / loaf of rice

A p. 31

a glass of	a piece of	a bowl of
water	cake	rice
juice	pizza	soup
milk	cheese	cereal

B p. 31

1. a bowl of — cake
2. a piece of — rice
3. a cup of — tea
4. a glass of — water
5. a bar of — soap
6. a can of — coke

Fun Wrap-Up! p. 32

Menu
- a bowl of rice
- a piece of cheese
- a bottle of juice
- a loaf of bread
- a glass of water

복수

p. 33

Quick Check-Up

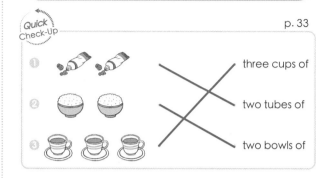

1. — three cups of
2. — two tubes of
3. — two bowls of

A p. 34

1. I drink two bottles of wine. — O
2. I buy three bowls of toothpaste. — X
3. She eats four pieces of cake. — O
4. I need four cups of coffee. — O
5. They have five glasses of soup. — X

B p. 34

1. Mom buys two __loaves of__ bread.
2. Dad drinks two __cups of__ tea.
3. I eat three __pieces of__ cheese.
4. He has two __bowls of__ rice.
5. We need four __glasses of__ milk.
6. I buy two __cans of__ coke.

Fun Wrap-Up! p. 35

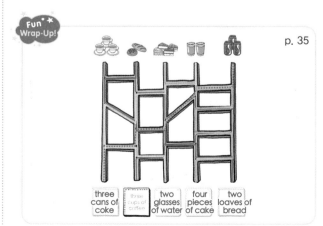

| three cans of coke | three cups of coffee | two glasses of water | four pieces of cake | two loaves of bread |

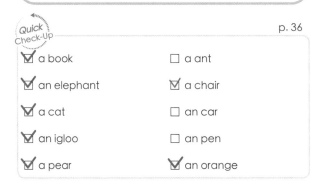

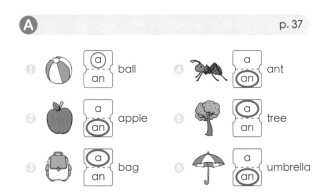

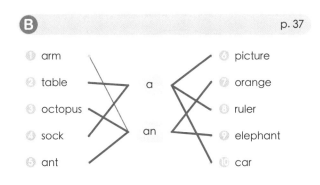

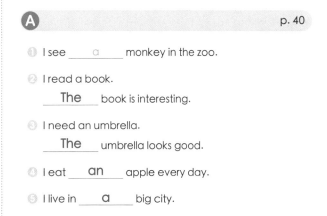

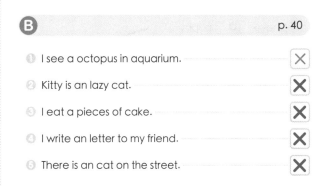

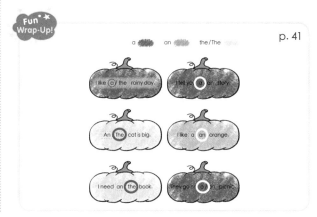

Lesson 06 관사

부정관사 a, an

Quick Check-Up p. 36

- ☑ a book
- ☑ an elephant
- ☑ a cat
- ☑ an igloo
- ☑ a pear
- ☐ a ant
- ☑ a chair
- ☐ an car
- ☐ an pen
- ☑ an orange

A p. 37

① a ball
② an apple
③ a bag
④ an ant
⑤ a tree
⑥ an umbrella

B p. 37

① arm
② table
③ octopus
④ sock
⑤ ant
⑥ picture
⑦ orange
⑧ ruler
⑨ elephant
⑩ car

Fun Wrap-Up! p. 38

an apple   a car   an umbrella
a hat   a mouse
an elephant   an ant   a bird

a, an, the

Quick Check-Up p. 39

① I want (a) an book.
② My mom wants (a) an dog.
③ I see a / (an) elephant.
④ She likes an / (the) short stories.

A p. 40

① I see ___a___ monkey in the zoo.
② I read a book.
   ___The___ book is interesting.
③ I need an umbrella.
   ___The___ umbrella looks good.
④ I eat ___an___ apple every day.
⑤ I live in ___a___ big city.

B p. 40

① I see a octopus in aquarium. ✗
② Kitty is an lazy cat. ✗
③ I eat a pieces of cake. ✗
④ I write an letter to my friend. ✗
⑤ There is an cat on the street. ✗

Fun Wrap-Up! p. 41

a   an   the / The

I like (a) the rainy day.   I tell yo a (an) story.
An (The) cat is big.   I like a (an) orange.
I need an (the) book.   They go o a (an) picnic.

Answers 153

Lesson 07 정관사

정관사 the (1)

Quick Check-Up
p. 42

1. I see (a)/ the dog. A /(The) dog is black.
2. I see (a)/ the girl. A /(The) girl drinks water.
3. I see (an)/ the elephant. An /(The) elephant sleeps.
4. There is (a)/ the boy. A /(The) boy eats an ice cream.

A
p. 43

1. I see a cat. A̶ cat is cute.   The cat is cute.
2. Look at a̶ bird in the sky.   Look at the bird in the sky.
3. Lock a̶ door, please.   Lock the door, please.
4. I see a dog. A̶ dog is big.   The dog is big.
5. Open a̶ window.   Open the window.

B
p. 43

1. I have __a__ puppy.
2. I know __the__ answers.
3. There is a duck in the river.
   __The__ duck is white.
4. I want __a__ puppy.
5. Look at __the__ moon.

a

an

the

Fun Wrap-Up!
p. 44

John wants _o_ comic book.

He goes to **the** Fun Comic bookstore.

He looks at many comic books there.

He sees one comic book.

He picks **the** comic book.

He likes **the** comic book.

He buys **the** comic book.

정관사 the (2)

Quick Check-Up
p. 45

☑ the sun   ☑ to the east
☑ play the piano   ☑ the moon
☐ have the dinner   ☑ study math
☑ Mike   ☑ to the right
☐ play the tennis   ☐ have the lunch

A
p. 46

1. The balloon is in the air. ⬭ O
2. My sister lives in the Japan. ✗
3. I have the breakfast. ✗
4. You go to the right. O
5. Suzy plays the piano. O
6. I play the tennis. ✗

B
p. 46

1. There is moon /(the moon) in the sky.
2. I throw a ball in air /(the air).
3. We eat out for (dinner)/ the dinner .
4. My brother plays (basketball)/ the basketball .
5. I study (English)/ the English very hard.

Fun Wrap-Up!
p. 47

Help me find a banana, please.

A
p. 48

1 I want _____ book.
ⓛ two   ② an   **③ a**

2 She eats _____ orange.
ⓛ a   **② an**   ③ two

3 I know _____ answers.
ⓛ a   **② the**   ③ an

4 She has two _____.
ⓛ babys   **② babies**   ③ babyes

5 _____ love toys.
ⓛ Children   ② Childs   ③ Childes

B
p. 48

1 I see _____**a**_____ monkey in the zoo.

2 I read a book. _____**The**_____ book is interesting.

3 I eat _____**an**_____ apple every day.

4 She plays _____**the**_____ piano.

C
p. 49

1 a watermelon. / want / They
They want a watermelon.

2 parents. / are / These / my
These are my parents.

3 mom's birthday / My / is / in February.
My mom's birthday is in February.

4 We / four / milk. / glasses of / need
We need four glasses of milk.

D *Answers vary.*
p. 49

1 What do you eat every day?
I eat an apple every day.

2 How many teeth do you have?
I have 26 teeth.

3 When is your birthday?
My birthday is in July.

4 What day is it today?
It is Friday.

단수: I, you, he/she/it

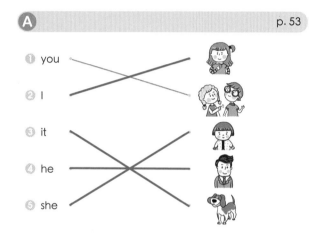

he | I | it | you | she

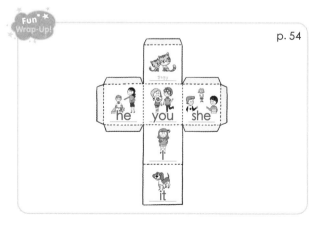

복수: we, you, they

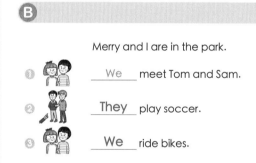

Merry and I are in the park.

1. ___We___ meet Tom and Sam.
2. ___They___ play soccer.
3. ___We___ ride bikes.

주격 대명사, 목적격 대명사

주격 대명사

p. 58

Quick Check-Up

① (I) like my bike.
② (He) likes apples.
③ (They) go home.
④ (They) can swim.
⑤ (We) play in the park.
⑥ (They) sing a song.
⑦ (It) is a cute pet.
⑧ (He) loves you.

A
p. 59

① (We) have lunch together.
② (He) likes cats.
③ (They) buy a bike.
④ (I) like my white shirt.

B
p. 59

① You are at the party. — Yes, I am.
② He is at the party. She is also at the party.
③ You are at the party. — Yes, we are.

Fun Wrap-Up!
p. 60

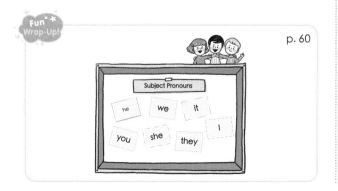

Subject Pronouns
he we it
you she they I

목적격 대명사

p. 61

Quick Check-Up

① I like (him).
② He likes (it).
③ Tom loves (us).
④ She hates (it).
⑤ They love (her).
⑥ We like (you).
⑦ You call (me).
⑧ I see (them).

A
p. 62

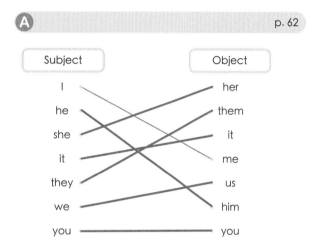

Subject	Object
I	her
he	them
she	it
it	me
they	us
we	him
you	you

B
p. 62

① I see him, but __he__ doesn't see __me__.
② They see me, but __I__ don't see __them__.
③ You see them, but __they__ don't see __you__.

Fun Wrap-Up!
p. 63

Subject Object

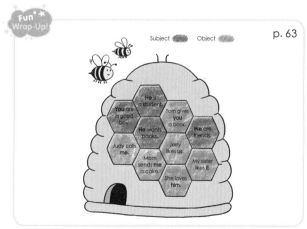

You are a good boy.
He is a student.
Tom gives you a book.
He wants books.
We are friends.
Judy calls me
Jerry likes us
Mom sends me a cake.
My sister likes it.
She loves him.

소유격

p. 64

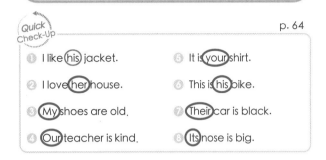

① I like (his) jacket.
② I love (her) house.
③ (My) shoes are old.
④ (Our) teacher is kind.
⑤ It is (your) shirt.
⑥ This is (his) bike.
⑦ (Their) car is black.
⑧ (Its) nose is big.

A p. 65

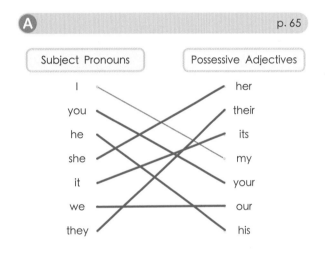

Subject Pronouns — Possessive Adjectives

I — her
you — their
he — its
she — my
it — your
we — our
they — his

B p. 65

① It's ___her___ pen. (she)
② It's ___my___ cat. (I)
③ It's ___your___ bag. (you)
④ It's ___his___ dog. (he)
⑤ These are ___their___ books. (they)

Fun Wrap-Up! p. 66

① Tom, which is your bag?
This is ___my___ bag.
② Which is Ann's bag?
This is ___her___ bag.
③ Which is Paul's bag?
This is ___his___ bag.
④ Which is Kate's bag?
This is ___her___ bag.

소유대명사

p. 67

hers — yours — yours — theirs — his
(mine) — (ours) — ours — (his) — (hers)

A p. 68

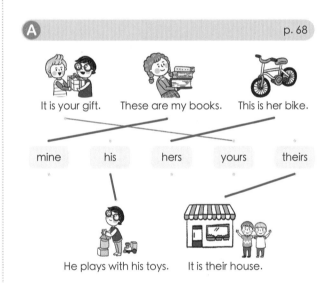

It is your gift.   These are my books.   This is her bike.

mine   his   hers   yours   theirs

He plays with his toys.   It is their house.

B p. 68

① This is ~~my book~~.   This is mine.
② It is ~~Tom's house~~.   It is his.
③ ~~Her shirt~~ is blue.   Hers is blue.
④ They are ~~your socks~~.   They are yours.

Fun Wrap-Up! p. 69

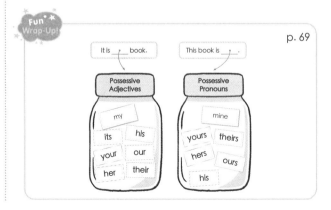

It is ___ book.   This book is ___.

Possessive Adjectives
my   its   his   your   our   her   their

Possessive Pronouns
mine   yours   theirs   hers   ours   his

this, that

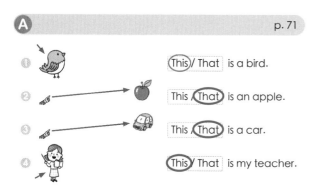

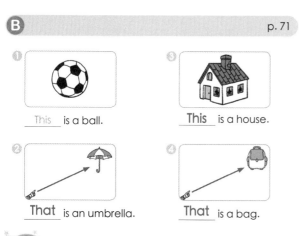

these, those

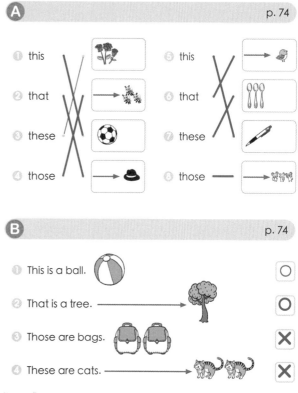

A
p. 76

1 I see him, but _____ doesn't see _____ .
   ① you, we   ② (he, me)   ③ him, he

2 You see them, but _____ don't see _____ .
   ① I, she   ② (they, you)   ③ You, I

3 Her shirt is blue. → _____ is blue.
   ① (Hers)   ② His   ③ Yours

4 It is Tom's house. → It is _____ .
   ① mine   ② hers   ③ (his)

5 They are your socks. → They are _____ .
   ① (yours)   ② theirs   ③ mine

B
p. 76

1 __This__ is a bird.

2 __That__ is a tree. ⟶

3 __Those__ are cats. ⟶

4 __These__ are bags.

C
p. 77

1 meet / We / Tom and Sam.
   We meet Tom and Sam.

2 white shirt. / I / like / my
   I like my white shirt.

3 their / are / books. / These
   These are their books.

4 my / Those / are / sisters.
   Those are my sisters.

D Answers vary.
p. 77

1 What color is your shirt?
   Mine is white.

2 Do you like that color?
   Yes, I do.

3 What color is your bag?
   It is blue.

4 What is your favorite color?
   My favorite color is red.

주어의 인칭에 따른 변화

Quick Check-Up · · · p. 80

1. He — am / are / **is**
2. She — am / are / **is**
3. I — **am** / are / is
4. It — am / are / **is**
5. You — am / **are** / is
6. We — am / **are** / is
7. They — am / **are** / is

A · · · p. 81

1. She are a girl. — ☐
2. I am pretty. — ✓
3. You're kind. — ✓
4. We is friends. — ☐
5. They're robots. — ✓
6. I'm a singer. — ✓
7. She is tall. — ✓
8. He are happy. — ☐
9. It are fun. — ☐
10. We are family. — ✓

B · · · p. 81

1. I ~~are~~ a girl. — I am a girl.
2. He ~~are~~ a doctor. — He is[He's] a doctor.
3. They ~~is~~ my friends. — They are[They're] my friends.
4. It ~~are~~ a cat. — It is[It's] a cat.
5. We ~~is~~ teachers. — We are[We're] teachers.

Fun Wrap-Up! · · · p. 82

주어의 수에 따른 변화

Quick Check-Up · · · p. 83

- ☑ It is a book.
- ☑ They are books.
- ☐ Jane are pretty.
- ☑ Water is cold.
- ☑ Those are red.
- ☐ A book are old.
- ☐ These is bags.
- ☑ Love is sweet.

A · · · p. 84

1. The balls **are** new.
2. The sky **is** blue.
3. It **is** long.
4. You **are** smart.
5. Lisa **is** kind.
6. Those **are** books.
7. They **are** sad.
8. She **is** brave.

B · · · p. 84

1. It **is** my birthday.
   My friends **are** at my party.
   They **are** happy.

2. You **are** happy today.
   These gifts **are** for you.
   The birthday party **is** so fun.

Fun Wrap-Up! · · · p. 85

Be동사: 부정문

am not, are not, is not

Quick Check-Up   p. 86

☐ They not are hungry.   ☑ The king is not powerful.

☐ A banana not is red.   ☑ The pencil is not long.

☑ She is not kind.   ☐ We not are in the store.

☑ The baby is not cute. ☑ He is not a doctor.

A
p. 87

❶ It is a dog.   ↻ It is not a dog.

❷ You are students.   ↻ You are not students.

❸ We are angels.   ↻ We are not angels.

❹ He is kind.   ↻ He is not kind.

❺ I am a writer.   ↻ I am not a writer.

B
p. 87

❶ I ____am not short____ . (short)

❷ Math is ____not easy____ . (easy)

❸ She is ____not sick____ . (sick)

❹ They are ____not girls____ . (girls)

❺ You ____are not ugly____ . (ugly)

❻ We ____are not teachers____ . (teachers)

Fun Wrap-Up!
p. 88

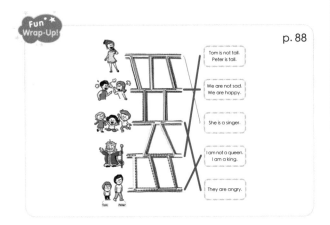

Tom is not tall. Peter is tall.

We are not sad. We are happy.

She is a singer.

I am not a queen. I am a king.

They are angry.

aren't, isn't

Quick Check-Up   p. 89

❶ You are not tall.   You aren't tall.

❷ He is not a singer.   He isn't a singer.

❸ Jane is not happy.   Jane isn't happy.

❹ We are not angry.   We aren't angry.

❺ Tom and Sam are not sad.   Tom and Sam aren't sad.

A
p. 90

❶ She isn't a painter. ───── ◯

❷ She isn't angry. ───── ◯

❸ They arenot nurses. ───── ✗

❹ I amn't heavy. ───── ✗

❺ These aren't my sisters. ───── ◯

B
p. 90

❶ They ____aren't____ students.

❷ Sam ____isn't____ in the gym.

❸ We ____aren't____ in London.

❹ The dog ____isn't____ under the table.

❺ I ____am not____ in the country.

❻ You ____aren't____ twelve years old.

❼ She ____isn't____ a dancer.

Fun Wrap-Up!
p. 91

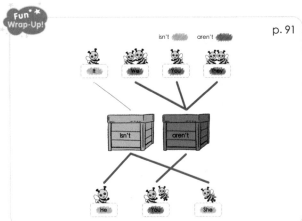

Lesson 14 — Be동사: 의문문

질문하기

Quick Check-Up   p. 92

- ☐ I am ten years old.
- ☑ Are they your pencils?
- ☐ My pets are sweet.
- ☐ The baby is cute.
- ☑ Are you strong?
- ☐ I am hungry.
- ☐ They are books.
- ☑ Are you there?

A   p. 93

1. <u>Is</u> he a doctor?
2. <u>Are</u> you in the classroom?
3. <u>Are</u> they friends?
4. <u>Is</u> Lisa at home?
5. <u>Is</u> that Nick?

B   p. 93

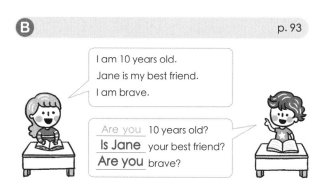

I am 10 years old.
Jane is my best friend.
I am brave.

<u>Are you</u> 10 years old?
<u>Is Jane</u> your best friend?
<u>Are you</u> brave?

Fun Wrap-Up!   p. 94

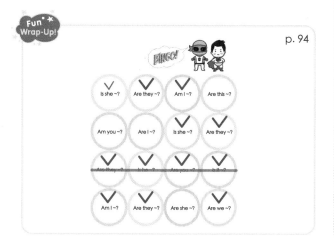

대답하기

Quick Check-Up   p. 95

1. Is Sam tall?
   - ☐ Yes, he is.   ☑ No, he isn't.
2. Is Tom tall?
   - ☑ Yes, he is.   ☐ No, he isn't.

A   p. 96

1. Is he a doctor? — Yes, he is.
2. Are you hungry? — No, I'm not.
3. Are we smart? — Yes, you are.
4. Are they pencils? — No, they aren't.
5. Is it short? — No, it isn't.

B   p. 96

1. Is she Lucy? — Yes, she is.
2. Is she nine years old? — Yes, she is.
3. Is she from France? — Yes, she is.
4. Is she a teacher? — No, she isn't.

Fun Wrap-Up!   *Answers vary.*

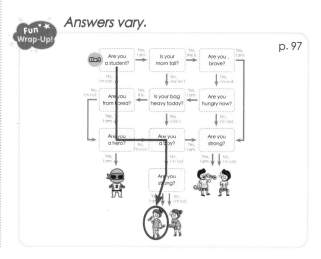   p. 97

일반동사

sing, drink, eat ...

p. 98

p. 99

A

1. I (play) soccer.
2. They (read) books.
3. They (eat) bananas.
4. I (drink) water.
5. You (sleep) on the bed.
6. You (have) a ball.
7. I (like) English.
8. You (go) to school.
9. I (dance).
10. They (come) home.

p. 99

B

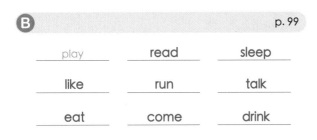

play	read	sleep
like	run	talk
eat	come	drink

p. 100

Fun Wrap-Up!

sings, drinks, eats ...

p. 101

1. I (drink)/ drinks water.
2. You (sing)/ sings .
3. She cry /(cries).
4. He swim /(swims).
5. I (work)/ works .
6. They (read)/ reads books.
7. He teach /(teaches) Math.
8. They (cook)/ cooks pasta.
9. She wash /(washes) a car.
10. He sleep /(sleeps).

p. 102

A

1. It __sounds__ great.   sound /(sounds)
2. I __watch__ TV.   (watch)/ watches
3. He __drinks__ coffee.   drink /(drinks)
4. A monkey __climbs__ up a tree.   climb /(climbs)
5. A rose __smells__ sweet.   smell /(smells)

p. 102

B

1. He ~~run~~ fast.   He runs fast.
2. She ~~watch~~ the movie.   She watches the movie.
3. He ~~write~~ a letter.   He writes a letter.
4. She ~~like~~ to read books.   She likes to read books.
5. The baby ~~cry~~.   The baby cries.

p. 103

Fun Wrap-Up!

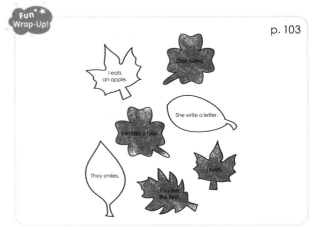

일반동사: 부정문

do not[don't]

p. 104

☑ I do not cry.　　☐ I does not eat pizza.

☑ They don't swim.　　☐ They doesn't jump.

☐ You doesn't smile.　　☑ You don't run.

☑ We do not walk.　　☐ We does not sleep.

A

p. 105

① You ___don't have___ a ball. (have)

② They ___don't read___ books. (read)

③ We ___don't cry___ . (cry)

④ I ___don't play___ the piano. (play)

⑤ I ___don't watch___ TV. (watch)

B

p. 105

① do not / swim. / We　　We do not swim.

② They / smile. / do not　　They do not smile.

③ like / pizza. / do not / I　　I do not like pizza.

④ I / drink / do not / water.　　I do not drink water.

⑤ run. / do not / You　　You do not run.

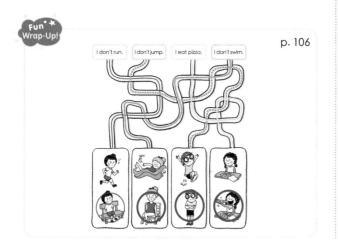

p. 106

I don't run. | I don't jump. | I eat pizza. | I don't swim.

does not[doesn't]

p. 107

☑ It doesn't rain.

☐ He does not speaks English well.

☑ My dog does not run fast.

☐ She do not eat hamburgers.

☑ The boy does not play baseball.

☐ She doesn't cleans her room.

A

p. 108

① My friend (does not)/ do not like chocolate.

② He (does not)/ do not make a boat.

③ She (does not)/ do not teach Korean.

④ Judy (does not)/ do not dance.

⑤ Tom (does not)/ do not drink coffee.

⑥ The man (does not)/ do not go shopping.

B

p. 108

① He ___doesn't drive___ a car. (drive)

② She ___doesn't listen___ to music. (listen)

③ Mom ___doesn't move___ . (move)

④ A snake ___doesn't walk___ . (walk)

⑤ Tom ___doesn't study___ math. (study)

p. 109

He don't run. | He doesn't run. | She don't cry. | She don't swim. | She doesn't swim. | I doesn't sleep. | I don't sleep. | We doesn't study.

일반동사: 의문문

질문하기

p. 110

Quick Check-Up

❶ (Does)/ Do she run fast?

❸ Does (Do) they dance?

❷ (Does)/ Do she draw?

❹ Does /(Do) you watch TV?

A
p. 111

❶ You run fast. ➡ _Do you_ run fast?

❷ He buys a cake. ➡ **Does he buy** a cake?

❸ She sleeps. ➡ **Does she** sleep?

❹ They play tennis. ➡ **Do they** play tennis?

❺ They watch TV. ➡ **Do they** watch TV?

B
p. 111

❶ ~~Does~~ they go to school? **Do they go to school?**

❷ ~~Do~~ she ~~likes~~ oranges? _Does she like oranges?_

❸ ~~Does~~ you drink milk? **Do you drink milk?**

❹ Does he ~~plays~~ baseball? **Does he play baseball?**

❺ ~~Does~~ we have a pen? **Do we have a pen?**

❻ ~~Do~~ she hurt her leg? **Does she hurt her leg?**

You can answer.
p. 112

Fun Wrap-Up!

Do you read a book? / Does he cry? / Does she listen to music?

(Yes, I do.) (Yes, he does.) (Yes, she does.)

대답하기

p. 113

Quick Check-Up

☐ Yes, I does. ☑ Yes, he does.

☐ No, she don't. ☐ No, they doesn't.

☑ Yes, she does. ☐ Yes, Tom do.

☑ No, we don't. ☐ No, I do.

A
p. 114

❶ Do you like soccer? - Yes, I _do_ .

❷ Does Tom study math? - Yes, he **does** .

❸ Do they sing? - No, they **don't[do not]**

❹ Does he jump? - No, he **doesn't[does not]**

❺ Does your sister sleep? - Yes, she **does** .

❻ Do you play the piano? - No, I **don't[do not]**

B
p. 114

❶ work? / Does / he _Does he work?_

❷ he / No, / doesn't. **No, he doesn't.**

❸ you / like / Do / carrots? **Do you like carrots?**

❹ I / do. / Yes, **Yes, I do.**

❺ Does / write / she / a letter? **Does she write a letter?**

Fun Wrap-Up!
p. 115

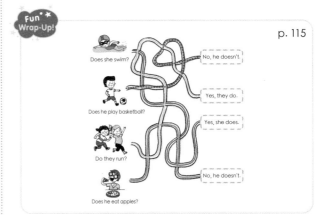

Does she swim? — No, he doesn't.
Does he play basketball? — Yes, they do.
Do they run? — Yes, she does.
Does he eat apples? — No, he doesn't.

A p. 116

1 I _____ a girl.
   ① is   ②(am)   ③ are

2 You _____ kind.
   ①(are)   ② is   ③ am

3 She _____ sick.
   ① are not   ② am not   ③(is not)

4 These _____ my sisters.
   ① isn't   ②(aren't)   ③ am not

5 Are you hungry? - _____
   ①(No, I'm not.)   ② Yes, he is.   ③ No, I amnot.

B p. 116

1 You __sleep__ on the bed.

2 He __teaches__ math.

3 The boy __does not__ play baseball.

4 __Does__ she hurt her leg? - Yes, she __does__.

C p. 117

1 gifts / are / These / for you.
   These gifts are for you.

2 is / easy. / not / Math
   Math is not easy.

3 under / The dog / isn't / the table.
   The dog isn't under the table.

4 the classroom? / you / Are / in
   Are you in the classroom?

D *Answers vary.* p. 117

1 Are you strong?
   No, I am not.

2 Do you study English?
   Yes, I do.

3 Are you 9 years old?
   Yes, I am.

4 Do you like pizza?
   No, I don't.

Answers **167**

형용사란?

p. 120

Quick Check-Up

① happy / (sad)

③ (sunny) / cloudy

② (clean) / dirty

④ (round) / square

A
p. 121

① I have a (cute) dog.

② She has (short) hair.

③ He is a (kind) boy.

④ Judy is a (good) student.

⑤ I drink (cold) water.

⑥ I am (hungry).

⑦ They are (nice) people.

⑧ This is a (new) book.

⑨ It is a (blue) desk.

⑩ We have a (big) bag.

B
p. 121

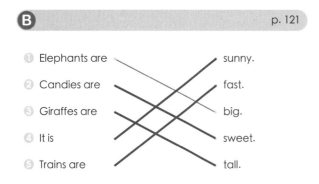

① Elephants are — big.

② Candies are — sweet.

③ Giraffes are — tall.

④ It is — sunny.

⑤ Trains are — fast.

Fun Wrap-Up!
p. 122

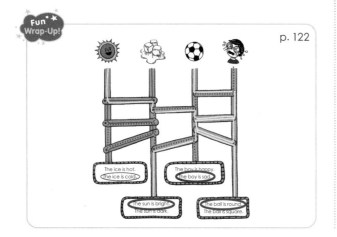

The ice is hot. / **The ice is cold.**

The boy is happy. / **The boy is sad.**

The sun is bright. / The sun is dark.

The ball is round. / The ball is square.

형용사의 위치

p. 123

Quick Check-Up

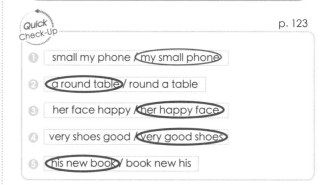

① small my phone / (my small phone)

② (a round table) / round a table

③ her face happy / (her happy face)

④ very shoes good / (very good shoes)

⑤ (his new book) / book new his

A
p. 124

① I have a ___short___ pencil. (short) / slow

② They are very ___good___ students. round / (good)

③ My classroom is ___clean___. (clean) / kind

④ Dogs are ___cute___. (cute) / sunny

⑤ My mom's car is ___new___. hungry / (new)

B
p. 124

① My bike / old. / is → My bike is old.

② tall. / Her brother / is → **Her brother is tall.**

③ water. / cold / This is / very → **This is very cold water.**

④ black. / is / Your pen → **Your pen is black.**

⑤ I / blue / pants. / have → **I have blue pants.**

⑥ has / She / good / a / pen. → **She has a good pen.**

Fun Wrap-Up! *Answers vary.*
p. 125

She has long hair.

My bag is green.

The man is tall.

The table is round.

지시형용사

p. 126

Quick Check-Up

① this ball / **these balls**
② **that car** / those cars
③ **this mouse** / these mice
④ that flower / **those flowers**

A
p. 127

① **this** / these pencil
② that / **those** houses
③ this / **these** books
④ **that** / those flower
⑤ this / **these** apples
⑥ that / **those** oranges
⑦ **this** / these girl
⑧ that / **those** rulers
⑨ **this** / these man
⑩ **that** / those building

B
p. 127

① This cat is cute. ○ _These cats_ are cute.
② That building is tall. ○ **Those buildings** are tall.
③ This house is nice. ○ **These houses** are nice.
④ That dog is black. ○ **Those dogs** are black.
⑤ This bird is small. ○ **These birds** are small.
⑥ That ruler is long. ○ **Those rulers are long** .

Fun Wrap-Up!
p. 128

지시대명사

p. 129

Quick Check-Up

① This is your clock.
→ **This clock** / These clock is yours.
② That is my book.
→ Those book / **That book** is mine.
③ These are white dogs.
→ Those dogs / **These dogs** are white.

A
p. 130

① This is my pen. ○ _This pen_ is mine.
② Those are nice hats. ○ **Those hats** are nice.
③ These are old books. ○ **These books** are old.
④ That is a new eraser. ○ **That eraser** is new.
⑤ This is a fast car. ○ **This car** is fast.

B
p. 130

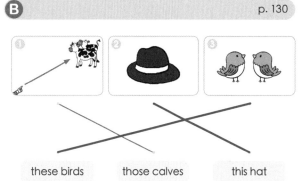

these birds   those calves   this hat

Fun Wrap-Up!
p. 131

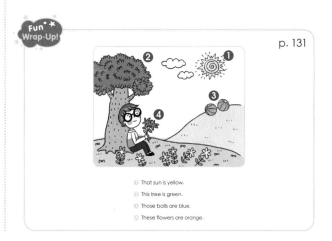

① That sun is yellow.
② This tree is green.
③ Those balls are blue.
④ These flowers are orange.

many, much, a lot of

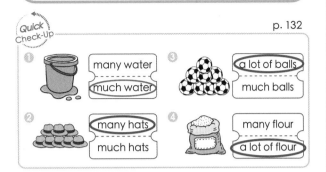

few, a few, little, a little

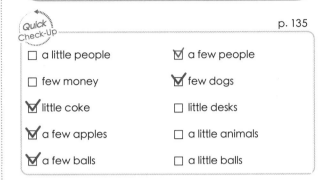

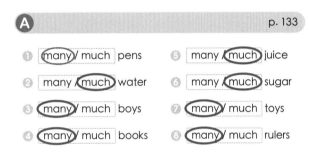

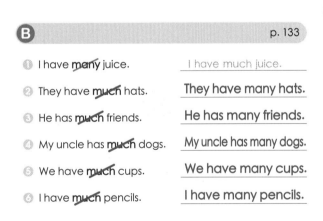

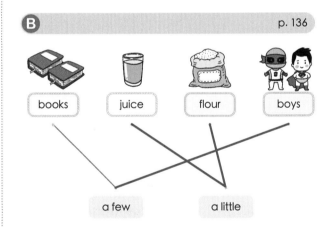

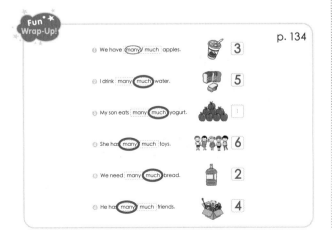

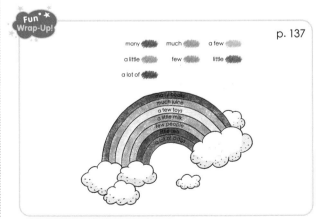

some, any

Quick Check-Up   p. 138

① I have ___some___ juice.

② We don't have **any** cats.

③ Do you have **any** candies?

④ She has **some** pants.

A   p. 139

① I have (some)/ any bananas.

② We need (some)/ any milk.

③ Do you have some /(any) questions?

④ I don't have some /(any) candies.

⑤ I make (some)/ any bread.

B   p. 139

① We don't have some soup. ────── ✕

② I don't need some water. ────── ✕

③ Do you have any sisters? ────── ○

④ I don't have some friends. ────── ✕

⑤ I have some bags in my room. ────── ○

Fun Wrap-Up!   p. 140

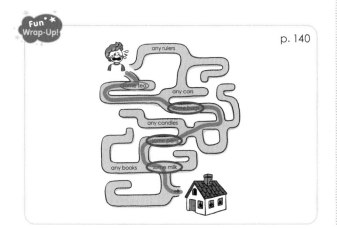

every, all

Quick Check-Up   p. 141

① (All)/ Every boys are hungry.

② All /(Every) boy is hungry.

③ All /(Every) child is sad.

④ (All)/ Every children are sad.

⑤ (All)/ Every books are interesting.

⑥ All /(Every) book is interesting.

⑦ (All)/ Every flowers are pretty.

⑧ All /(Every) flower is pretty.

A   p. 142

① ___All___ the boys are students.

② She likes **all** kinds of movies.

③ **Every** house has a door.

④ **All** children go to school.

⑤ I play the piano **every** day.

B   p. 142

① All animals sleep.   ○ Every animal sleeps.

② All roses are red.   ○ **Every rose is red.**

③ All horses have four legs. ○ **Every horse has four legs.**

④ All cars are clean.   ○ **Every car is clean.**

⑤ All trains are long.   ○ **Every train is long.**

Fun Wrap-Up!   p. 143

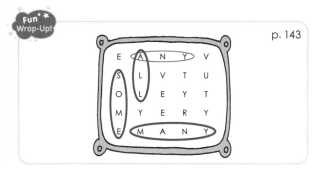

Basic Test

A
p. 144

1 Look at _____ face.
   ① her happy ② happy her ③ she happy

2 _____ are cute.
   ① This cats ② That cat ③ These cats

3 He has _____ friends.
   ① a ② many ③ much

4 I have _____ apples.
   ① much ② a few ③ little

5 I have _____ water.
   ① little ② few ③ a few

B
p. 144

1 I don't have _____ any _____ money.

2 I have _____ some _____ juice.

3 _____ Every _____ man is busy.

4 _____ All _____ students eat lunch.

C
p. 145

1 people. / are / They / nice
   They are nice people.

2 birds / Those / small. / are
   Those birds are small.

3 have / many / I / pencils.
   I have many pencils.

4 good / are / very / These / shoes.
   These are very good shoes.

D *Answers vary.*
p. 145

1 How many erasers do you have?
   I have three erasers.

2 Do you have short hair or long hair?
   I have short hair.

3 Do you have any sisters?
   No, I don't.

4 Do you have any red pants?
   Yes, I do.

Activity Cards & Paper Cube

Lesson 04 p. 29

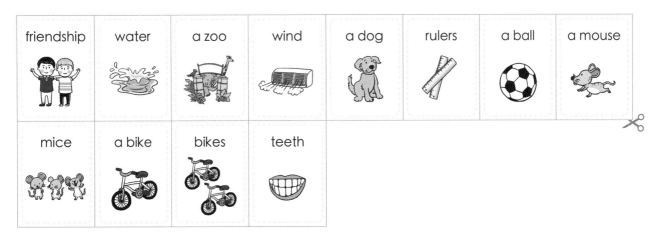

friendship	water	a zoo	wind	a dog	rulers	a ball	a mouse

mice	a bike	bikes	teeth

Lesson 08 p. 54

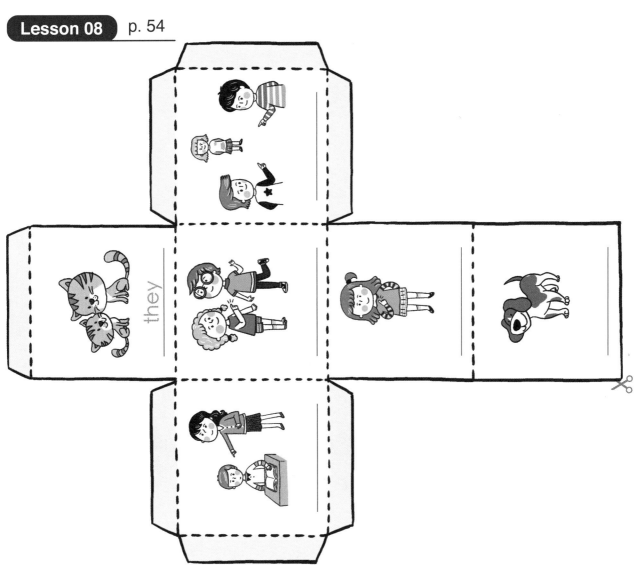

Activity Cards & Paper Cube

Lesson 09 p. 60

he	boy	we	it	dog	hot
I	you	for	girl	she	they

Lesson 10 p. 69

its	his	yours	your	their
our	theirs	my	his	hers
mine	her	ours		

Lesson 12 p. 85

That	Water	We	Love	Leaves	A book
A frog	These	Apples	Coffee	Tom and Jim	Those
He	This	Jim	She	The sky	It
Cats	Tom	They	A dog	Bees	A pig